The World's Wit and Humor

The World's Wit and Humor

An Encyclopedia of the Classic Wit and Humor of all Ages and Nations

American, British, French, German, Italian, Spanish, Russian, Scandinavian, Greek, Roman, Oriental and Miscellaneous

Fifteen Volumes, with Portrait Frontispieces and Many Cartoons

International Board of Editors

Joel Chandler Harris
American

Andrew Lang
British

Brander Matthews
Continental European

William Hayes Ward
Greek, Roman and Oriental

Horatio Sheafe Krans, *Associate American*

Lionel Strachey, *Managing Editor*

New York
The Review of Reviews Company
1910

Николай Гоголь

The World's Wit and Humor

RUSSIAN

SCANDINAVIAN

Miscellaneous

Volume XIV
Khemnitzer to Gorki

Holberg to Strindberg

Erasmus to Sienkiewicz

New York
The Review of Reviews Company
1910

Miscellaneous Wit and Humor

Dutch

Hungarian

Table of Contents

Miscellaneous Wit and Humor

Lettish

Servian

Rumanian

Haytian

West Indian Negro

Acknowledgment

We beg to tender courteous acknowledgment to SMALL, MAYNARD & COMPANY for the use of " Love and Bread," by AUGUST STRINDBERG.

Russian, Scandinavian, and Miscellaneous Wit and Humor

Russian Wit and Humor

Ivan Khemnitzer

The Philosopher

A CERTAIN rich man, who had heard it was an advantage to have been at school abroad, sent his son to study in foreign parts. The son, who was an utter fool, came back more stupid than ever, having been taught all sorts of elaborate explanations of the simplest things by a lot of academical windbags. He expressed himself only in scientific terms, so that no one understood him, and every one became very tired of him.

One day, while walking along a road, and gazing at the sky in speculating upon some problem of the universe to which the answer had never been found (because there was none), the young man stepped over the edge of a deep ditch. His father, who chanced to be near by, ran to get a rope. The son, however, sitting at the bottom of the ditch, began to meditate on the cause of his fall. He concluded that *an earthquake had superinduced a momentary displacement of his corporeal axis, thus destroying his equilibrium, and, in obedience to the law of gravity as established by Newton, precipitating him downward until he encountered an immovable obstacle*—namely, the bottom of the ditch.

When his father arrived with the rope, the following dialogue took place between them:

"I have brought a rope to pull you out with. There, now, hold on tight to that end, and don't let go while I pull."

"A rope? Please inform me what a rope is before you pull."

3

"A rope is a thing to get people out of ditches with, when they have fallen in and can't get out by themselves."

"But how is it that no mechanical device has been constructed for that purpose?"

"That would take time; but you will not have to wait until then. Now, then——"

"Time? Please explain first what you mean by time."

"Time is something that I am not going to waste on a fool like you. So you may stay where you are until I come back."

Upon which the man went off, and left his foolish son to himself.

Now, would it not be a good thing if all eloquent windbags were gathered together and thrown into the ditch, to keep him company? Yes, surely. Only it would take a much larger ditch than that to hold them.—*The " Fables."*

The Lion's Council of State

A LION held a court for state affairs.
Why? That is not your business, sir—'twas theirs.
He called the elephants for councilors. Still
The council-board was incomplete,
And the king deemed it fit
With asses all the vacancies to fill.
Heaven help the state, for lo! the bench of asses
The bench of elephants by far surpasses.
"He was a fool, th' aforesaid king," you'll say;
"Better have kept those places vacant, surely,
Than to have filled 'em up so very poorly."

4

Ivan Khemnitzer

Oh, no, that's not the royal way;
Things have been done for ages thus, and we
Have a deep reverence for antiquity.
Naught worse, sir, than to be, or to appear,
Wiser and better than our fathers were!
The list must be complete, e'en though you make it
Complete with asses—for the lion saw
Such had through all the ages been the law.
He was no radical to break it;
" Besides," said he, " my elephants' good sense
Will soon my asses' ignorance diminish,
For wisdom has a mighty influence."
They made a pretty finish!
The asses' folly soon obtained the sway:
The elephants became as dull as they!

—The " Fables."

The House-Builder

A CERTAIN man a house would build.
The place is with materials filled,
And everything is ready there;
Is it a difficult affair?
Yes, till you fix the corner-stone;
It won't erect itself alone.
Day rolls on day, and year on year,
And nothing yet is done;
There's always something to delay
The business to another day.

And thus in silent waiting stood
The heaps of stone and piles of wood,

Till Death—who in his vast affairs
Ne'er puts things off (as men in theirs),
And thus, if I the truth must tell,
Does his work finally and well—
Winked at our hero as he passed:
"Your house is finished, sir, at last—
A narrower house, a house of clay,
Your palace for another day!"

—The "Fables."

Alexander Griboyedov

Muscovite Society

Famusov, Skalozub, *and* Chatski.

Fam. (*to* Skalozub). I wonder, by the way, how we are related. There's no legacy for us to fight about, though. Your cousin once told me how you were related to Nastasya Nikolaevna, but I have forgotten.

Skal. I—er—really don't know; we were not in the same regiment.

Fam. What a pity! I would do anything for a relative. Yes, I would hunt the world for a relative, just to find him and do something for him. Why, nearly all my official subordinates are nephews of mine, or some other near relatives. Of course one always thinks of one's family when there is any prospect of promotion or a decoration. But your cousin told me he did very well in the army through you.

Skal. We served together against Bonaparte in the Thirtieth Cavalry, and afterward in the Forty-fifth, with—er— some credit.

Fam. Dear me, fancy having a relative like that! He wears a ribbon in his buttonhole, if I am not mistaken.

Skal. Ah, yes—for a little affair in a trench; we held a trench together, you know. And then we each got a medal.

Fam. Your cousin is a splendid chap, to be sure!

Skal. Oh, his head is stuffed with new-fangled ideas!

7

Russian Wit and Humor

Just as he was going to be promoted, he left the army, and settled down in the country to read a lot of books.

Fam. What a peculiar fellow! You, however, have done the right thing. But you have been colonel for some time, though you have not been in the service so very long.

Skal. Oh, I don't know; I've had fairly good luck; some of the men have been pensioned off, and others killed.

Fam. Yes, the Lord watches over his own!

Skal. But some have done better than I. Take my brigadier-general, for instance.

Fam. Well?

Skal. Oh, it's not of that—er—I am complaining, you know. No, I cannot say I have been passed over—though I have been with my regiment for two years now.

Fam. I see; you want to be a general. But you have left a number of your colleagues behind, it seems to me.

Skal. Yes, I admit that I want to be a general. There are different ways of getting promotion, and I don't care which way I get mine, so long as I become a general.

Fam. Quite right. I wish you good luck and the rank of general. And, by the by, is it not time for you to think of marriage?

Skal. Well—er—I don't know; I should not mind.

Fam. There are plenty of chances here—any quantity of sisters and nieces and daughters to choose from. Oh, yes, all the opportunity you could wish for in Moscow. Yes, Moscow is a wonderful city, you must admit.

Skal. The distances are very great.

Fam. We are governed by good taste here, and by admirable rules and fine old traditions. For instance, there is a venerable custom of judging a man by his father. He may be a good-for-nothing sort of fellow, but if he has a couple

8

of thousand serfs, that makes him an eligible match. Another might have more ability and pride, and that sort of thing—well, let him pass for a clever fellow. But we don't want him in our families. No, no; we have a decent respect for birth. Besides, look at our hospitality—especially toward foreigners. They are always welcome, whether they have a good reputation or not. You can always tell a Muscovite when you see one. At fifteen or sixteen our youngsters know more than their teachers. As for our old men, you should hear them discuss things. Such wisdom! Such liberality! It would never do for their criticisms of the government to be published. Not that they ever suggest an innovation. Oh, dear, no! They simply find fault with this and that, or with nothing at all. They get warmed up, and make a good fuss, and then go home. Every one of them ought to be a cabinet minister. And the women! There is nothing they cannot do, from playing cards to commanding armies and managing politics. See what admiration the King of Prussia expressed for our girls when he was here—for their accomplishments, not their faces. Show me girls brought up better than ours! They know how to dress in any sort of clothes; they twist their mouths into the proper shape when they speak; they sing French songs, and dwell on the high notes; they are devoted to the military, because they are so patriotic. Yes, I must say it would be difficult to find another capital like Moscow!

Skal. The fire improved it a great deal, I think.

Fam. Quite so. Since the fire, our roads, our footwalks, our houses, all creak in a new fashion.

Chat. The houses are new, but the prejudices are old. Let us rejoice! Neither time, nor change, nor fires will ever do away with them!

Fam. (*aside to* CHATSKI). Hush! Keep quiet! Can't you remember? (*To* SKALOZUB.) Allow me to make you acquainted with my friend Chatski—the son of the late Andrey Ilich, you know. He is not in the government service; he does not care about it. It is a pity, too, because he would make a good official. He is a young man of high intelligence, and he writes a good hand, and translates well. I cannot help regretting——

Chat. Never mind your regrets!

Fam. Oh, but everybody else is of the same opinion about you!

Chat. What do I care for their opinions? A lot of old fossils with an invincible hatred against freedom, whose *opinions* are derived from newspapers dating back to the conquest of the Crimea! They are always ready to find fault; it's always the same old song with them; and the older they grow the worse they get—only they never know it. Where are the reverend sires whom we are to look up to as examples? Those who have grown rich by jobbery and corruption, who escape the law through family patronage, who build fine palaces where they live in wasteful luxury? Pray, who is there in Moscow whose mouth has not been shut by dinners, suppers, and balls? Should it be he to whom I was taken as a mere suckling, for some incomprehensible reason, to make humble obeisances—that archscoundrel surrounded by a host of sycophants? They did everything in the world to please him, and more than once saved his honor and his life when he was besotted in his filthy debauches. And then what did he do for them? Gave them up for three dogs! Or that other worthy, who, to gratify a whim, had cart-loads of children torn away from their parents to dance before him in a ballet. Yes, he, and

Alexander Griboyedov

all Moscow, looked on and clapped their hands while the nymphs and cupids danced! But that did not satisfy his creditors. Nymphs and cupids were sold off by degrees, every one of them. And these are the old men whose gray hairs we are to respect, who are to be the arbiters of our conduct and sit in judgment upon us! But if only one of our young men, hating servility, and wanting neither place nor promotion, gives himself up to science or devotes his whole soul to art, immediately they raise the hue and cry against him: Murder! Help! Look at the dangerous dreamer! The uniform—there is nothing beyond the uniform; their horizon is limited by gold braid and brass buttons; and what was good enough for them is good enough for us. And it's the same thing with their wives and daughters: Nothing like the uniform!—*"Wo from Wit."*

Traditional Fairy Tale

The Sluggard

ON the banks of a certain river, where there was always good fishing, lived an old man and his three sons. The two eldest were sharp-witted, active young men, already married; the youngest was stupid and idle, and a bachelor. When the father was dying, he called his children to him and told them how he had left his property. The house was for his two married sons, with a sum of three hundred rubles each. After his death he was buried with great pomp, and after the funeral there was a splendid feast. All these honors were supposed to be for the benefit of the man's soul.

When the elder brothers took possession of their inheritance they said to the youngest, "Listen, brother; let us take charge of your share of the money, for we intend going out into the world as merchants, and when we have made a great deal of money we will buy you a hat, a sash, and a pair of red boots. You will be better off at home; and mind you do as your sisters-in-law tell you."

For a long time this silly fellow had been wanting a cap, a sash, and a pair of red boots, so he was easily persuaded to give up all his money.

The brothers set out on their travels, and crossed the sea in search of fortune. The "fool" of the family remained at home; and as he was an out-and-out sluggard, he would lie whole days at a time on the warm stove without doing a stroke of work, and only obeying his sisters-in-law with the greatest reluctance. He liked fried onions, potato soup, and cider, better than anything else in the world.

One day his sisters-in-law asked him to fetch them some water.

It was winter, and there was a hard frost; moreover, the sluggard did not feel at all inclined to go out. So he said, "Go yourselves; I prefer to stay here by the fire."

"Stupid boy, go at once! We will have some onions, potato soup, and cider ready for you when you come back. If you refuse to do what we ask you we shall tell our husbands, and then there will be neither cap, sash, nor red boots for you."

At these words the sluggard thought he had better go. So he rolled off the stove, took a hatchet and a couple of pails, and went down to the river. On the surface of the water, where the ice had been broken, was a large pike. The sluggard seized him by the fins and pulled him out.

"If you will let me go," said the pike, "I promise to give you everything you wish for."

"Well, then, I should like all my desires to be fulfilled the moment I utter them."

"You shall have everything you want the moment you pronounce these words:

"'At my behest, and by the orders of the pike,
    May such and such things happen, as I like.'"

"Just wait one moment while I try the effect," said the sluggard, and began at once to say:

"'At my behest, and by the orders of the pike,
    Bring onions, cider, soup, just as I like.'"

13

That very moment his favorite dishes were before him. Having eaten a large quantity, he said, "Very good! Very good indeed! But will it always be the same?"

"Always," replied the pike.

The sluggard put the pike back into the river, and, turning toward his buckets, said:

"At my behest, and by the orders of the pike,
Walk home yourselves, my pails—that I should like."

The pails, and the strong rod to which they were fastened, immediately set off and walked solemnly along, the sluggard following them with his hands in his pockets. When they reached the house he put them in their places, and again stretched himself out to enjoy the warmth of the stove. Presently the sisters-in-law said, "Come and chop some wood for us."

"Bother! Do it yourselves."

"It is not fit work for women. Besides, if you don't do it the stove will be cold, and then you will be the chief sufferer. Moreover, pay attention to what we say, for if you do not obey us, there will be no red boots, nor any other pretty things."

The sluggard then just sat up, and said:

"At my behest, and by the orders of the pike,
Let what my sisters want be done—that's what I like."

Instantly the hatchet came out from behind a stool and chopped up a large heap of wood, put a part of it on the stove, and retired to its corner. All this time the sluggard was eating and drinking at his ease.

Another day some wood had to be brought from the forest. Our sluggard now thought he would like to show off before the villagers, so he pulled a sledge out of the shed, loaded it with onions and soup, after which he pronounced the magic words.

The sledge started off, and passing through the village at a rattling pace, ran over several people, and frightened the women and children.

When the forest was reached, our friend looked on while the blocks of wood and fagots cut, tied, and laid themselves on the sledge, after which they set off home again. But when they got to the middle of the village, the men who had been hurt and frightened in the morning seized hold of the sluggard and pulled him off the sledge, dragging him along by the hair to give him a sound thrashing.

At first he thought it was only a joke, but when the blows hurt his shoulders, he said:

"At my behest, and by the orders of the pike,
   Come, fagots, haste, and my assailants strike."

In a moment all the blocks of wood and fagots jumped off the sledge and began to hit right and left, and they hit so well that the men were glad to get out of the way as best they could.

The sluggard laughed at them till his sides ached; then he remounted his sledge, and was soon lying on the stove again.

From that day he became famous, and his doings were talked about all through the country.

At last even the king heard of him, and, his curiosity being aroused, he sent some of his soldiers to fetch him.

"Now, then, booby," said the soldier, "come down off that stove and follow me to the king's palace."

"Why should I? There is as much cider, onions, and soup as I want at home."

The man, indignant at his want of respect, struck him.

Upon which the sluggard said:

> "At my behest, and by the orders of the pike,
> May this man get a taste of what a broom is like."

A large broom, and not particularly clean, immediately hopped up, and, first dipping itself in a pail of water, beat the soldier so mercilessly that he was obliged to escape through the window, whence he returned to the king. His Majesty, amazed at the sluggard's refusal, sent another messenger. This man was cleverer than his comrade, and first made inquiries as to the sluggard's tastes. Then he went up to him and said, "Good day, friend; will you come with me to see the king? He wishes to present you with a cap, a sash, and a pair of red boots."

"With the greatest pleasure. You go on; I will soon overtake you."

Then he ate as much as he could of his favorite dishes, and went to sleep on the stove. He slept so long that at last his sisters-in-law woke him up and told him he would be late if he did not at once go to see the king. The lazy fellow said nothing but these words:

> "At my behest, and by the orders of the pike,
> This stove to carry me before the king I'd like."

At the very same instant the stove moved from its place and carried him right up to the palace door. The king was filled with amazement, and, running out, followed by the whole court, asked the sluggard what he would like to have.

"I have merely come to fetch the hat, sash, and red boots you promised me."

Just then the charming Princess Gapiomila came to find out what was going on. Directly the sluggard saw her, he thought her so enchanting that he whispered to himself:

> "At my behest, and by the orders of the pike,
> That this princess so fair may love me, I should like."

Then he ordered his stove to take him back home, and when there he continued to eat onions and soup and to drink cider.

Meanwhile the princess had fallen in love with him, and begged her father to send for him again. As the sluggard would not consent, the king had him bound when asleep, and thus brought to the palace. Then he summoned a cele-brated magician, who at his orders shut the princess and sluggard up in a crystal cask, to which was fastened a bal-loon well filled with gas, and sent it up in the air among the clouds. The princess wept bitterly, but the fool sat still and said he felt very comfortable. At last she persuaded him to exert his powers, so he said:

> "At my behest, and by the orders of the pike,
> This cask of crystal earth at once do strike
> Upon the friendly island, I should like."

The crystal cask immediately descended, and opened upon a hospitable island where travelers could have all they wanted by simply wishing for it. The princess and her com-panion walked about, eating when hungry and drinking when thirsty. The sluggard was very happy and contented, but the lady begged him to wish for a palace. Instantly the palace made its appearance. It was built of white marble, with crystal windows, roof of yellow amber, and golden furniture. She was delighted with it. Next day she wanted a good road made, along which she could go to see her father. Immediately there stretched before them a fairy-like bridge made of crystal, having golden balustrades set with diamonds, and leading right up to the king's palace. The sluggard was just about to accompany the princess when he began to think of his own appearance, and to feel ashamed that such an awkward, stupid fellow as he should walk by the side of such a lovely and graceful creature; so he said:

"At my behest, and by the orders of the pike,
    To be both handsome, wise, and clever I should like."

Suddenly he became as handsome, wise, and clever as it was possible to be. Then he got into a gorgeous carriage with Gapiomila, and they drove across the bridge that led to the king's palace.

There they were received with every mark of joy and affection. The king gave them his blessing, and they were married the same evening.—*Chodsko's " Anthology."*

Ivan Krylov

The Swan, the Pike, and the Crab

WHENE'ER companions don't agree,
  They work without accord;
And naught but trouble doth result,
  Although they all work hard.

One day a swan, a pike, a crab,
  Resolved a load to haul;
All three were harnessed to the cart,
  And pulled together all.
But though they pulled with all their might,
The cart-load on the bank stuck tight.
The swan pulled upward to the skies;
  The crab did backward crawl;
The pike made for the water straight—
  It proved no use at all!

Now, which of them was most to blame,
  'Tis not for me to say;
But this I know: the load is there
  Unto this very day.

—The " Fables."

The Musicians

THE tricksy monkey, the goat, the ass, and bandy-legged Mishka, the bear, determined to play a quartet. They provided themselves with the necessary instruments—two fiddles, an alto, and a bass. Then they all settled down under a large tree, with the object of dazzling the world by their artistic performance. They fiddled away lustily for some time, but only succeeded in making a noise, and no music.

"Stop, my friends!" said the monkey, "this will not do; our music does not sound as it ought. It is plain that we are in the wrong positions. You, Mishka, take your bass and face the alto; I will go opposite the second fiddle. Then we shall play altogether differently, so that the very hills and forests will dance."

So they changed places, and began over again. But they produced only discords, as before.

"Wait a moment!" exclaimed the ass; "I know what the matter is. We must get in a row, and then we shall play in tune."

This advice was acted upon. The four animals placed themselves in a straight line, and struck up once more.

The quartet was as unmusical as ever. Then they stopped again, and began squabbling and wrangling about the proper positions to be taken. It happened that a nightingale came flying by that way, attracted by their din. They begged the nightingale to solve their difficulty for them.

"Pray be so kind," they said, "as to stay a moment, so that we may get our quartet in order. We have music and we have instruments; only tell us how to place ourselves."

To which the nightingale replied:

" To be a musician, one must have a better ear and more intelligence than any of you. Place yourselves any way you like; it will make no difference. You will never become musicians."—*The " Fables."*

D. V. Davidov

Wisdom

WHILE quaffing the grape's ruby nectar,
  All sportingly, laughingly gay,
We determined—I, Silvya, and Hector—
  To drive old dame Wisdom away.

" Oh, my children, take care ! " said the beldame;
  " Attend to these counsels of mine :
Get not tipsy, for danger is seldom
  Remote from the goblet of wine."

" With thee in his company, no man
  Can err," said our wag, with a wink;
" But come, thou good-natured old woman,
  Take a pull at our flagon, and drink ! "

She frowned, but her scruples soon twisting,
  Consented, and smilingly said :
" So polite—there's indeed no resisting,
  And Wisdom was always well-bred."

She drank, but continued her teaching :
  " Let the wise from indulgence refrain; "
And never gave over her preaching
  But to say, " Fill my goblet again."

D. V. Davidov

And she drank, and she tottered, but still she
    Was talking, and shaking her head,
Mutt'ring " Temperance," " Prudence," until she
    By Folly was carried to bed.

Nikolai Gogol

Defunct Serfs as an Investment

ONE of the commissions given to Chichikov was to arrange
with the owner of a certain estate for the mortgaging of a
number of his serfs to the financial institution called the
Council of Guardians. Chichikov found this proprietor to
be on the verge of ruin. The cattle had been thinned out
by an epidemic disease, there had been several meager har-
vests, a lot of the most industrious field laborers had died
off, overseers had been dishonest, and the lord of the manor
himself had been grossly extravagant, fitting up a large
house in Moscow, so that the estate was now drained to the
last copeck. . . .

Chichikov elicited the information that since the last government census a considerable number of the serfs had died,
but that their names had not been removed from the census
list. To all intents and purposes, therefore, those peasants
could be counted as alive. It was upon this discovery that
Chichikov was inspired with the most brilliant idea that
ever originated in a human mind. Said our hero to himself:

" What a fool I am! I have been looking for my spectacles, and they are on my nose! Why, all I have to do is
to buy the serfs who have died since the last census was
taken! If I purchase a thousand of them, and the Council
of Guardians pays me two hundred rubles per soul, I shall
then have a capital of two hundred thousand rubles. There
has been a great deal of sickness of late, and, thank the
Lord, a high rate of mortality. The landowners have been

throwing their money away at cards, and wasting it in riotous living. Everybody has been seized with the craze for town life and service under the government. The estates are neglected or abandoned by the landlords, who find it harder every year to squeeze money out of them to pay the taxes. This seems to be my chance for earning an honest sum. It will take a lot of trouble, and I must avoid a scandal. There is the obstacle, too, that without land one can neither buy nor mortgage serfs. But I know what I will do: I will buy them ostensibly for colonization. There are provinces such as Kherson where land is given free to settlers. I will take up land in Kherson, and pack off all my dead peasants there. The whole thing can be done in conformity with the legal requirements." . . .

"Allow me, sir, to ask you a question," said Chichikov to Manilov, speaking with a rather strange intonation, at the same time looking furtively about him. The person addressed, without any apparent reason, also cast furtive glances about the room, until the other continued:

"How long ago do you think it is since you handed in your last census report?"

"A long time ago, I should say; I really don't remember."

"But a good many of your serfs have died since then?"

"I could not say. I suppose I shall have to ask the overseer."

The overseer having been sent for, Manilov asked him:

"Listen, my good man: how many of our serfs have died since the last count was taken?"

"Eh? How many? Why, a good many," replied the overseer, stifling a yawn.

"That's just what I thought myself," said the landlord.

"Yes, that's it—a good many have died." And turning to Chichikov, he added, "Precisely so, a great many."

"What might the number be, for instance?" inquired Chichikov.

"Ah, yes, what number?" echoed Manilov.

"The number—the number, did you say?" queried the overseer. "Why, I don't know how many have died. No one has counted them."

"That's it exactly," said Manilov to his guest. "I thought a good many must have died, but I haven't the least idea of the number."

"Would you mind having a list of them made, with the name of each one?"

"Yes, with the name of each one," said Manilov.

Whereupon the overseer answered, "Yes, sir," and left the room.

When he had gone, the host observed:

"What do you want this done for?"

Chichikov appeared to be embarrassed by this question. His features assumed an awkward expression, and he even blushed in the effort to explain himself.

"You want to know the reason—the reason?" stammered Chichikov. "The reason is—I—I should like to buy some serfs."

"Well, then, let me ask you, sir, how you wish to buy them: with the land, or without the land—for exportation?"

"It is not exactly that kind I want. I mean serfs who are dead."

"What do you say? Excuse me, please, but I did not hear very well. I do not quite understand."

"I propose," said Chichikov, "to purchase from you serfs

who are actually no longer living, but whose names still appear in the official census records."

Manilov's pipe dropped to the floor. Its owner sat staring stark at Chichikov for several minutes in complete silence. At last he picked up his pipe, and then, for a space, gazed intently at his guest, wondering whether he had not gone out of his mind. But he saw no external signs of insanity. Manilov was quite at a loss what to think or do, so he stopped thinking, and did nothing but puff out a thin stream of smoke from between his lips.

"I should like to know, you see," resumed our hero, "whether you would be willing to make over to me some souls who, though really dead, are legally in existence."

But Manilov was so astonished and confused that he could still do nothing but stare and blow out smoke.

"Well, do you see any difficulty about it?"

"Do I see any difficulties?" was the reply. "Oh, no, not at all; but you must excuse me—I don't understand. I have not enjoyed such an education as yours, I might say. I have not your beautiful way of expressing my thoughts, I might say. Perhaps, in what you have just been good enough to say, perhaps there is some hidden meaning; perhaps you chose that particular way of speaking for—for the sake of literary style."

"No, no; I mean just what I told you—souls who are actually dead."

Manilov was entirely dumfounded. He must take some course, say something, ask some question—only, what question? But all he did was to puff out more smoke—this time through his nose.

"If there are no objections, then, suppose we draw up a deed of sale," suggested Chichikov.

"What! a deed of sale of dead souls?"

"By no means," replied Chichikov. "We will treat them as if they were alive—as they are, according to the census report. Heaven forbid that I should in any way transgress against the law! Let us conform to the law. I bow to the majesty of the law."—"*Dead Souls.*"

Letters of a Lap-Dog

I PUT on my old cloak and took my umbrella because it was pouring rain. There was no one in the streets. I saw only a few women with shawls over their heads, and some shopkeepers with umbrellas. There was no one of the upper classes about, except one official like myself. I saw him at a crossing, and said to myself, "Aha! No, my friend, you're not going to the department; you're running after the woman in front of you, and looking at her ankles." What a set of brutes our officials are! They're just as bad as any officer; can't see a woman's hat without going for it. Just as I was thinking that, I saw a carriage driving up to a shop I was passing. I knew it at once; it was our director's carriage. "But he wouldn't be going shopping," I thought; "it must be his daughter." I stopped, and leaned against the wall; a footman opened the carriage-door, and she sprang out like a bird. How she glanced round with those eyes of hers! Heaven defend me! I am done for! And why ever should she drive out in this pouring rain? And then people say that women are not devoted to finery! She did not recognize me, and, indeed, I purposely muffled myself up, because my cloak was very muddy, and old-fashioned too.

Now they are worn with deep capes, and mine had little capes one above the other; and the cloth wasn't good either. Her lap-dog didn't get in before the shop-door was shut, and was left out in the street. I know that dog; it is called Medji. The next minute I suddenly heard a little voice, " Good morning, Medji." Why! what the deuce did it mean? Who said that? I looked round, and saw two ladies under an umbrella—an old lady and a young one; but they went past. Suddenly I heard again, " Oh, for shame, Medji! " The devil! There were Medji and the ladies' lap-dog smelling each other. " I say," thought I to myself, " I must be drunk! " And yet it is a rare thing with me to be drunk. " No, Fidèle, you are quite mistaken "—I actually saw Medji saying that—" I have been—bow-wow-wow—I have been— bow-wow-wow—very ill."

Well, there, now! I really was very much surprised to hear the lap-dog talking in human speech. But afterward, when I thought it over, it didn't astonish me. Indeed, there have been many such cases in the world. It is said that there appeared in England a fish that said two words in such a strange language that the learned men have been three years trying to make out what it said, and can't understand it yet. And I remember reading in the newspapers about two cows that went into a shop and asked for a pound of tea. But I was very much more astonished when Medji said, " I wrote to you, Fidèle; Polkan can't have brought the letter." Well! may I lose my salary if ever I heard in my life that dogs could write! It quite amazed me. Lately, indeed, I have begun to see and hear things that nobody ever saw or heard before.

" I'll follow that lap-dog," thought I, " and find out what it is, and what it thinks." So I shut up my umbrella and followed the two ladies. They went along Gorokhovaya Street, turned into Myeshchanskaya Street, then into a carpenter's shop, and at last up to the Kokoushkin Bridge, and there they stopped before a big house. "I know that house," said I to myself; "that's Tvyerkov's house." What a monster! Just to think of the numbers of people who live there —such a lot of strangers, and servant-maids; and as for my fellow officials, they are packed together like dogs! I have a friend living there who plays the trumpet very well. The ladies went up to the fifth story. "All right," thought I, "I won't go in now, but I will mark the place, and take advantage of the first opportunity." . . .

At two o'clock in the afternoon I started to find Fidèle and interrogate her. I can't endure cabbage, and all the little provision-shops in Myeshchanskaya Street simply reek of it; and then there's such a stench from the yard of every house, that I simply held my nose and ran along as fast as ever I could. And then those confounded artisans send out such a lot of soot and smoke from their workshops, that really there's no walking in the street. When I got up to the sixth floor, and rang the bell, there came out a girl, not bad-looking, with little freckles. I recognized her; it was the same girl who had walked with the old lady. She grew a bit red, and inquired, "What can I do for you?" I answered, "I must have an interview with your lap-dog." The girl was stupid; I saw at once she was stupid. At that moment the dog ran out, barking. I wanted to catch her, but the nasty little thing nearly snapped my nose off. However, I saw her basket in the corner. Ah! that was what I wanted. I went up to it, turned over the straw, and, to my immense delight, found a package of tiny papers. Seeing that, the horrid little dog first bit me in the calf of the leg, and then, realizing that I had got the papers, began to whine and fawn on me. But I said, "No, my dear; good-by!" and rushed away. I think the girl took me for a maniac, for she was terribly frightened.

When I got home I wanted to set to work at once and read the letters, because my sight is not very good by candle-light. But, of course, Mavra had taken it into her head to wash the floor. These idiotic Finns are always cleaning at the wrong time. So I went for a walk to think over the occurrence. Now, at last, I shall find out all their affairs, all their thoughts, all the wires they are pulled by; these letters will disclose everything to me. Dogs are a clever race; they understand all the political relations; and so, no doubt, everything will be here—this man's portrait and all his affairs. And no doubt there will be something about her, who— Never mind—silence! In the evening I got home. I spent the time lying on my bed. . . .

Now let us see! The letter is fairly legible; but, somehow or other, there is something a little bit doggish about the handwriting. Let's see:

My dear Fidèle: I still have not been able to accustom myself to your vulgar name. Why couldn't they find a better name for you? Fidèle, Rosa, what bad taste! However, this is away from the point. I am very glad that we have agreed to correspond.

The letter is quite correctly written; there are no mistakes in the punctuation or even in the spelling. Why, the chief of the section can't write as well as that, although he talks about having been educated at the university. Let's see farther on:

It appears to me that to share our thoughts, feelings, and impressions with another is one of the greatest blessings in the world.

Hm—that idea is copied from some work translated from the German—I can't remember the title.

I say this from experience, although I have seen little of the world beyond the gates of our house. My life passes peacefully and happily. My mistress, whom papa calls Sophie, loves me passionately.

Oh! oh! Never mind—never mind! Silence!

Papa, too, often caresses me. I drink my tea and coffee with cream. Ah, *ma chère*, I must tell you that I cannot understand what pleasure there can be in the big gnawed bones that our Polkan devours in the kitchen. Bones are only good if they are from game, and if no one has sucked the marrow out of them. It is a very good idea to mix several kinds of sauce together, only there must be no capers or herbs; but I know nothing worse than the custom of rolling bread into little balls and giving it to dogs. Some gentleman, sitting at the table, who has been holding all sorts of nasty things in his hands, will begin rolling a bit of bread with his fingers, and then call you, and put it in your mouth. It's impolite to refuse, so you eat it—with disgust, of course, but you eat it.

What the deuce is all this rubbish? As if they couldn't find anything better to write about. Let's look at the next page; perhaps it will be more sensible.

I shall have the greatest pleasure in informing you of all that happens in our house. I have already spoken to you about the principal gentleman whom Sophie calls papa. He is a very strange man.

Ah, now, at last! Yes, I knew it. They look at all things from a political point of view. Let us see what there is about papa:

Strange man! He hardly ever speaks. But a week ago he kept on constantly saying to himself, "Shall I get it, or not?" Once he asked me, "What do you think, Medji? Shall I get it, or not?" I didn't understand anything about it, so I smelled at his boot and went away. Then, *ma chère*, a week afterward papa was in the greatest state of delight. The whole morning long gentlemen in uniform came to him and congratulated him on something or other. At table he was merrier than I have ever seen him before.

Ah, so he's ambitious! I must take note of that.

Good-by, *ma chère!* I must be off. To-morrow I will finish the letter.

Well, good morning; I am with you again. To-day, my mistress, Sophie——

Ah, now we shall see—something about Sophie. Oh! confound it!—Never mind, never mind! Let's go on:

My mistress, Sophie, was in a great muddle. She was getting ready for a ball, and I was very glad she would be out, so that I could write to you. My Sophie is perfectly devoted to balls, although she nearly always gets cross when she's dressing for them. I cannot conceive, *ma chère*, what can be the pleasure of going to balls. Sophie comes home from them at six o'clock in the morning, and nearly always looks so pale and thin that I can see at once they haven't given the poor girl anything to eat there. I confess that I couldn't live like that. If I didn't get my woodcock with sauce, or the wing of a roast chicken, I—really I don't know what I should do. I like pudding with sauce, too, but carrots or turnips or artichokes are no good at all.

What an extraordinarily uneven style! One can see at once it wasn't written by a human being; it begins all right and properly, and ends in this doggish fashion. Let's see another letter. This seems rather a long one. Hm—and it isn't dated.

Oh, my dearest, how I feel the approach of spring! My heart beats as if it yearned for something. There is a constant singing in my ears, so that I often raise one foot, and stand for several moments listening at a door. I will confide to you that I have many suitors. Oh! if you knew how hideous some of them are! Sometimes there's a great, coarse, mongrel watch-dog, fearfully stupid—you can see it written on his face—who struts along the street and imagines that he's a very important personage, and that everybody is looking at him. Not a bit of it! I take no more notice than if I didn't see him at all. Then, there's such a frightful mastiff that stops before my window. If he were to stand on his hind paws (which the vulgar creature probably doesn't know how to do) he'd be a whole head taller than my Sophie's papa, who is rather a tall man, and stout too. This blockhead appears to be frightfully impertinent. I growled at him, but he took no notice at all; he didn't even frown. He lolled out his tongue, hung down his monstrous ears, and stared in at the window—like a common peasant! But do you imagine, *ma chère*, that my heart is cold to all entreaties? Ah, no! If you could see one young beau who jumps across the fence from next door! His name is Trésor. Oh, my dearest, what a sweet muzzle he has!

The devil take it all! What rubbish! And fancy filling up one's letter with nonsense of that kind! Give me a man! I want to see a human being; I demand that spiritual food that would satisfy my thirsting soul, and instead of that, all this stuff! Let's see another page; perhaps it'll be better.

Sophie was sitting at the table sewing something. I was looking out of the window, because I like watching the passers-by. Suddenly a footman came in and announced, "Teplov." "Ask him in!" cried Sophie, and flew to embrace me. "Oh, Medji, Medji! if only you knew who it is: a chamberlain, dark, and with such eyes—quite black, and as bright as fire!" And she ran away to her room. A minute afterward there came in a young chamberlain, with black whiskers. He went up to the mirror, set his hair straight, and looked about the room. I growled, and sat down in my place. Presently Sophie came in, looking very happy. He clinked his spurs, and she bowed.   I pretended not to notice anything, and went on looking out of the window, but I turned my head a little on one side and tried to overhear their conversation.   Oh, *ma chère*, what rubbish they talked! They talked about how, at a dance, one lady had made a mistake and done the wrong figure; then about how a certain Bobov, with a large frill on his shirt, looked very like a stork, and nearly tumbled down; then about how a certain Lidina imagines that her eyes are blue, whereas they are green—and so on.   I cannot think, *ma chère*, what she finds in her Teplov.   Why is she so enchanted with him?

It seems to me, too, that there's something wrong here. It's quite impossible that Teplov could bewitch her so. What comes next?

Really, if she can like this chamberlain, it seems to me she might as well like the official who sits in papa's study.   Oh, *ma chère*, if you knew what a fright he is!   Exactly like a tortoise in a bag.

What official can that be?

He has a most peculiar name.   He always sits and mends pens. The hair on his head is very much like hay.   Papa always sends him on errands instead of the servant.

I believe that beastly little dog is alluding to me.   Now, *is* my hair like hay?

Sophie simply cannot keep from laughing when she looks at him.

You lie, you confounded dog!   What an abominable style! As if I didn't know that this is simply a case of envy; as if I didn't know it's an intrigue!   It's an intrigue of the chief of the section.   The man has sworn implacable hate against me, and now he does everything he can to injure me—to injure me at every step. Well, I'll look at just one more letter; perhaps the affair will explain itself.

MY DEAR FIDÈLE: Forgive me for having been so long without writing. I have been in a state of absolute intoxication. It is perfectly true what some writer has said, that love is second life. And then there are great changes going on in our house. The chamberlain comes every day now. Sophie is madly in love with him. Papa is very happy. I even heard from our Grigory, who sweeps the floors, and almost always talks to himself, that there will soon be a wedding, because papa is very anxious to see Sophie married, either to a general, or to a chamberlain, or a colonel.

Deuce take it all! I can read no more. A chamberlain or a general! I should like to become a general myself, not in order to obtain her hand or anything like that—no, I should like to be a general, only to see them put on all their airs and graces and show off all their court ways, and then tell them that I don't care a brass farthing for either of them. It really is annoying, confound it all!

I tore the silly little dog's letters into bits.

—"*A Madman's Diary.*"

Incognito

GOVERNOR, JUDGE, CHARITY COMMISSIONER, POSTMASTER, *and* CONSTABLE.

Post. Tell me, gentlemen, who's coming—what sort of official?

Gov. What, haven't you heard?

Post. I heard something from Bobchinski; he was just now with me at the post-office.

Gov. Well, what do you think about it?

Post. What do *I* think about it? Why, there'll be a war with the Turks.

Judge. Exactly; that's just what I thought!

Gov. Well, you're both wide of the mark.

Post. It'll be with the Turks, I'm sure. It's all the Frenchman's doing.

Gov. Pooh! war with the Turks, indeed! It's *we* who are going to get into trouble, not the Turks. That's quite certain. I've a letter to say so.

Post. Oh, then we sha'n't go to war with the Turks.

Gov. (*to the* POSTMASTER). Well, how do *you* feel?

Post. How do *I* feel? How do *you?*

Gov. I? Well, I'm no coward, but I *am* just a little uncomfortable. The shopkeepers and townspeople bother me. It seems I'm unpopular with them; but, the Lord knows, if I've blackmailed anybody, I've done it without a trace of ill-feeling. I even think (*buttonholes him, and takes him aside*)—I even think there will be some sort of complaint drawn up against me. Why should we have an inspector coming here at all? Look here, don't you think you could just slightly open every letter which comes in and goes out of your office, and read it—for the public benefit, you know— to see if it contains any kind of information against me, or only ordinary correspondence? If it is all right, you can seal it up again, or simply deliver the letter opened.

Post. Oh, I know *that* game! Don't teach me *that!* I do it from pure curiosity, not as a precaution; I'm death on knowing what's going on in the world. And they're very interesting to read, I can tell you! Now and then you come across a love-letter, with bits of beautiful language, and so edifying—much better than the *Moscow News!*

Gov. Tell me, then, have you read anything about any official from Petersburg?

Post. No, nothing about any one from Petersburg, but plenty about the Kostroma and Saratov people. It's a pity you don't read the letters. There are some very fine passages in them. For instance, not long ago a lieutenant writes to a friend, describing a ball in first-rate style—splendid! "Dear friend," he says, "I live in Elysium; heaps of girls, music playing, flags flying." Quite a glowing description, quite! I've kept it by me, on purpose. Would you like to read it?

Gov. Thanks; there's no time now. But oblige me, if ever you chance upon a complaint or a denouncement, by keeping it back, without the slightest compunction.

Post. I will, with the greatest pleasure.

Judge (who has overheard something). You had better mind; you'll get into trouble over that some time or other.

Post. (innocently). Eh? The saints forbid!

Gov. It was nothing—nothing. It would be different if it concerned you or the public; but it was a private affair, I assure you!

Judge (aside). Hm, *some* mischief was brewing, *I* know! (*To the* GOVERNOR.) But I was going to say that I had a puppy to make you a present of—own sister to the dog you know about. I dare say you've heard that Cheptovich and Varkhovinski have gone to law with each other. So now I live in clover; I hunt hares first on one fellow's estate, and then on the other's.

Gov. I don't care about your hares now, my good friend. I've got that cursed *incognito* on the brain! I expect the door to open, and all of a sudden——

Nikolai Gogol

Enter BOBCHINSKI *and* DOBCHINSKI, *out of breath.*

Bob.   What an extraordinary occurrence!

Dob.   An unexpected piece of news!

All.   What is it? What is it?

Dob.   Something quite unforeseen; we go into the inn——

Bob.   Yes, Dobchinski and I go into the inn——

Dob.   All right; let *me* tell it!

Bob.   No, no, allow me—allow me. You haven't got the knack——

Dob.   Oh, but you'll get mixed up and forget it all.

Bob.   Oh, no, I sha'n't—good heavens, no! There, don't interrupt me—*do* let me tell the news—don't interrupt! Pray oblige me, gentlemen, and tell Dobchinski not to interrupt.

Gov.   Well, say on, for God's sake, what is it? My heart is in my mouth! Sit down, gentlemen; take seats! (*They all sit round* BOBCHINSKI *and* DOBCHINSKI.) Well, now, what is it, what is it?

Bob.   Permit me—permit me; *I* can relate it properly. Hm—as soon as I had the pleasure of taking my leave after you were good enough to be bothered with the letter which you had received, sir—yes, then I ran out— Now, please don't keep on taking me up, Dobchinski; I know all about it, all, I tell you, sir.—So, as you'll kindly take notice, I ran out to see Karobkin. But not finding Karobkin at home, I went off to Rastakovski, and not seeing *him,* I went, you see, to the postmaster's to tell him of the news you'd got; yes, and going on from there I met Dobchinski——

Dob.   By the stall, where they sell tartlets——

39

Bob. ——by the stall, where they sell tartlets. Well, I meet Dobchinski and say to him, "Have you heard the news the governor has got? The letter may be depended on!" But he had already heard of it from your housekeeper, Avdotya, who, I don't know why, had been sent to Pachechuyev's——

Dob. With a bottle for some French brandy.

Bob. ——yes, with a bottle for some French brandy. Then I went with Dobchinski to Pachechuyev's— *Will* you stop, Dobchinski—there, *do* have done with your interfering! —So off we go to Pachechuyev's, and on our way Dobchinski says, "Let's go," says he, "to the hotel. I've eaten nothing since morning; there's such a rumbling in my inner man." Yes, sir, in Dobchinski's internals. "But they've got some fresh salmon at the hotel," he says; "so we can have a snack." We hadn't been in the hotel a moment when in comes a young man——

Dob. Rather good-looking and well-dressed.

Bob. ——yes, rather good-looking and well-dressed, and walks into the room, with such an expression on his face— such a physiognomy—and style—so distinguished a head-piece. I had a kind of presentiment, and I say to Dobchinski, "There's something up here, sir!" Yes, and Dobchinski beckoned, and called up the landlord, Vlas, the innkeeper, you know—three weeks ago his wife presented him with a baby, such a fine, forward boy—he'll grow up just like his father, and keep a hotel. Well, we called up Vlas, and Dobchinski asks him quite privately, "Who," says he, "is that young man?" And Vlas replies, "That," says he— "Oh, don't interrupt me so, Dobchinski, please; good Lord! *you* can't tell the story, you can't tell it—you don't speak plainly, with only one tooth in your head, and a lisp."

—" That young man," says he, " is an official "—yes, sir—
" who is on his way from St. Petersburg, and his name," says
he, " is Ivan Alexandrovich Khlestakov, sir, and he's off,"
says he, " to the government of Saratov," says he, " and his
goings-on are very peculiar. He's stayed here over a fortnight; he doesn't leave the house; he takes everything on
account, and doesn't pay a copeck." When he told me that,
I felt illuminated from above, and I said to Dobchinski,
" Hey! "

Dob. No, *I* said " Hey! "

Bob. Well, first *you* said it, and then *I* did. " Hey! "
said both of us, "and why does he stay here, when he's
bound for Saratov? " Yes, sir, that official is *he!*

Gov. Who—what official?

Bob. Why, the official of whom you were pleased to get
the notification—the Inspector-General.

Gov. Great God! *What* do you say? It *can't* be he!

Dob. It *is,* though! Why, he pays no money, and he
doesn't go. Who else could it be? And his order for post-
horses is made out for Saratov.

Bob. It's he, it's he! good God, it's he! Why, he's so
observant; he noticed everything. He saw that Dobchinski
and I were eating salmon—all on account of Dobchinski's
inside—and he looked at our plates like this (*imitates*). I
was in an awful fright.

Gov. Lord, have mercy upon sinners like us! Where is
he staying now, then?

Dob. In room No. 5, first floor.

Bob. In the same room where the officers quarreled last
year on their way through.

Gov. How long has he been here?

Dob. A fortnight or more. He came on St. Vasili's Day.

Gov. A fortnight! (*Aside.*) Holy Fathers and Saints, preserve me! In that fortnight the sergeant's wife was flogged! No provisions given to the prisoners! Dram-shops and dirt in the streets! Shameful! scandalous! (*Tears his hair.*)

Char. Com. (*to the* GOVERNOR). What do you think, had we better go to the inn in gala uniform?

Judge. No, no! First send the mayor, then the clergy and the tradespeople.

Gov. No, no! Leave it to me! I've had ticklish jobs before now, and I've managed 'em all right, and even been thankful for them. Maybe the Lord will help us out this time as well. (*Turns to* BOBCHINSKI.) You say he's a *young* man?

Bob. Yes, about twenty-three or four at the outside.

Gov. So much the better—it's easier to ferret a thing out. It's the devil, if you've got an old bird to deal with; but a young man's all on the surface. You, gentlemen, had better get your departments in order, while I'll go by myself, or with Dobchinski here, and have a private stroll round, to see that travelers are treated with due consideration. Here, constable!

Con. Sir?

Gov. Go at once to the Police Superintendent's; or no— I shall want you. Tell somebody to send him as quick as possible to me, and then come back here.

(CONSTABLE *runs out at full speed.*)

Char. Com. (*to* JUDGE). Let us go! Let us go! Some mischief may happen, I do believe.

Judge. What's there for *you* to be afraid of? Give the sick clean nightcaps, and the thing's done!

Char. Com. Nightcaps—bosh! The sick were ordered

Nikolai Gogol

to have oatmeal porridge. Instead of that, there's such a smell of cabbages in all my corridors that you're obliged to hold your nose.

Judge. Well, *my* mind's at ease on *that* score. As to the County Court, who'll visit *that?* Supposing he *does* look at any of the papers, he'll wish he'd left it alone. Why, I've been sitting fifteen years on the bench—and do I ever look at a charge-sheet? No, thank you! Solomon himself couldn't make head or tail of 'em!

. . . .

The same characters (except POSTMASTER*) with* DIRECTOR OF SCHOOLS *and* KAROBKIN, *an ex-official.*

Enter the POSTMASTER, *out of breath, with an opened letter in his hand.*

Post. Here's an astounding thing happened, gentlemen! The official we took to be the Inspector-General, is *not* an inspector!

All. What! *not* an inspector?

Post. Not an inspector at all. I've found that out from the letter.

Gov. What do you mean—what do you mean? from *what* letter?

Post. Why, from the letter he wrote *himself.* They bring me a letter to post. I look at the address, and see "Post-office Street." I was regularly stunned. Well, I say to myself, he's without doubt found something wrong in the postal department, and he's reporting it to the authorities. So I took the letter and—opened it.

Gov. How could you——

Post. I don't know—a supernatural force impelled me.

43

I had already ordered a courier to take it by express, but such a feeling of curiosity overpowered me as I had never known before. "I can't do it, I can't, I can't!" I hear myself saying; but I feel drawn, drawn to it! "Oh, don't open it, or you'll be utterly ruined!" that's what sounds in one ear; and in the other, like a devil whispering, "Open it! Open it! Open it!" And so I broke the sealing-wax —my veins were on fire; but after I had done it they froze—by God, they froze! My hands shook, and everything whirled.

Gov. And so you *dared* to open the letter of so powerful a personage?

Post. That's where the joke is! He's neither a personage nor powerful!

Gov. What *is* he, then, according to you?

Post. Neither the one nor the other; the devil knows *what* he is!

Gov. (furiously). What do you mean? How do you dare to call him neither the one nor the other, nor the devil knows what? I'll put you under arrest——

Post. Who? You?

Gov. Yes. *I* will!

Post. Pooh! That's beyond your power!

Gov. Are you aware that he is going to marry my daughter—that I shall become a grandee—that I shall have power to send people to Siberia?

Post. Eh, Governor, Siberia? That's a long way off. But I had better read you the letter.—Gentlemen, let me read it you!

All. Yes, read it, read it!

Post. (reads). "I hasten to let you know, my dear Tryapichkin, all about my adventures. On the way an infantry captain cleared me out completely, so that the innkeeper wanted to send me to jail; when, all of a sudden, owing to my Petersburg get-up and appearance, the whole town took me for the Governor-General. So now I am living at the Governor's. I do just as I please; I flirt madly with his wife and daughter—but I can't settle which to begin with. Do you remember how hard up we were, how we dined at other people's expense, and how the pastry-cook once pitched me out, neck and crop, because I had put some tarts I had eaten down to the account of the King of England? It is quite a different state of things now. They all lend me as much money as ever I please. They are an awful set of originals; you would die of laughing if you saw them! You write articles, I know: bring these people in. First and foremost, there's the Governor. He's as stupid as a mule——"

Gov. Impossible! It can't be there!

Post. (*showing him the letter*). Read it yourself!

Gov. (*reads*). "Stupid as a mule." It can't be so—you've written it yourself!

Post. How *could* I have written it?

Char. Com. Read!

Dir. of Schools. Read on!

Post. "——The Governor. He's as stupid as a mule——"

Gov. Oh, devil take it! Is it necessary to repeat *that?* As if it wasn't there without that!

Post. (*continues*). Hm—hm—hm—"as a mule. The Postmaster, too, is a good fellow—" (*Stops.*) Well, he says something uncomplimentary about *me,* too.

Gov. No—read it out!

Post. But what's the good?

Gov. No, no—confound it, if you read *any* of it, read it all! Read it through!

Char. Com. Allow me; I'll have a try! (*Puts on his spectacles, and reads.*) "The Postmaster is exactly like our office-beadle Mikheyev, and a rascal into the bargain. He drinks like a fish."

Post. Well, the young blackguard ought to be flogged—that's all!

Char. Com. (*continuing*). "The Charity Com—er—er—" (*Hesitates.*)

Karob. But what are you stopping for?

Char. Com. It's badly written. However, it's clearly something insulting.

Karob. Give it to me! My eyes are better, I fancy. (*Tries to take the letter.*)

Char. Com. (*holding it back*). No, we can leave that part out; farther on it's plain enough.

Karob. But allow me—I can read!

Char. Com. Why, so can *I!* Farther on, I tell you, it's quite easy to make out.

Post. No, read it all! It was all read before!

All. Give it up! Give the letter up! (*To* Karobkin.) You read it!

Char. Com. Certainly! (*Hands the letter.*) There, if you please. (*Covers the passage with his finger.*) *That's* where you begin. (*All crowd round.*)

Post. Read it, read it through! What nonsense! Read it *all!*

Karob. (*reading*). "The Charity Commissioner is a regular pig in a skullcap."

Char. Com. That's supposed to be *witty!* Pig in a skull-cap! Who ever saw a pig in a skullcap?

Karob. (*continues*). "The School Director reeks of onions——"

Nikolai Gogol

Dir. of Schools. Good God! Why, an onion has never crossed my lips!

Judge (*aside*). Thank goodness, there's nothing, at any rate, about *me!*

Karob. (*reading*). " The Judge——"

Judge (*aside*). Now for it! (*Aloud.*) I think this letter is tedious. What the devil's the good of reading all that rubbish?

Dir. of Schools. No!

Post. Go on with it!

Char. Com. No, read it through!

Karob. (*resumes*). " The Judge is in the utmost degree *mauvais ton.*" (*Stops.*) That must be *French!*

Judge. But the devil knows what's the meaning of it! It's bad enough if it's only *swindler,* but it may be a good deal worse.

Karob. (*goes on*). "' But, after all, the people are hospitable and well-meaning. Farewell, my dear Tryapichkin. I myself should like to follow your example and take up literature. It's a bore, my friend, to live as I do—one certainly wants food for the mind. One must, I see, have some elevated pursuit. Write to me at the village of Podkalitovka, Saratov government." (*He turns the letter over and reads the address.*) " To the Well-born and Gracious Ivan Vasiliyevich Tryapichkin, St. Petersburg, Post-office Street, Number Ninety-seven, within the Courtyard, Third Floor, on the right."

Gov. He has as good as cut my throat! I'm crushed, crushed—regularly crushed! I can see nothing—only pigs' snouts instead of faces, nothing else! Catch him! Catch him! (*Gesticulates wildly.*)

Post. How can we catch him? Why, as if on purpose

47

I told the manager to give him his very best sledge, and the devil persuaded me to give him an order for horses in advance.

Judge. Besides, sirs, confound it! he has borrowed three hundred rubles of me!

Char. Com. And three hundred of *me* too!

Post. Yes, and three hundred of me as well!

Bob. And Dobchinski and I gave him sixty-five, in bank-notes!

Judge. How was it, gentlemen, that we came to make such a mistake?

Gov. (*beats himself on the shoulders*). How *could* I? There's not such another old blockhead as I am! I must be in my dotage, idiot of a muttonhead that I am! Thirty years have I been in the service; not a tradesman or contractor could cheat me; rogue after rogue have I overreached, sharpers and rascals I have hooked, that were ready to rob the whole universe! Three governors-general I've duped! And look at me now, look—all the world, all Christendom, all of you, see how the Governor's fooled! Ass, booby, dotard that I am! (*Shakes his fists at himself.*) Ah, you fat-nose! Taking an icicle, a rag, for a man of rank! And now he's rattling along the road with his bells, and telling the whole world the story! Not only do you get made a laughing-stock of, but some quill-driver, some paper-stainer, will go and put you in a play! It's maddening! He'll spare neither your rank nor your profession, and all will grin and clap their hands. (*Stamps on the ground ferociously.*) I'd like to get my hands on the pack of scribblers! Ugh! The quill-splitters! Damned liberals! Devil's brood! I would throttle them all; I'd grind them to powder! (*Shakes his fist and grinds his heel on the ground.*

Then, after a short silence.) I can't collect myself yet. It's true, that if God intends to punish a man, he first drives him mad. To be sure, what was there like an inspector-general in that crack-brained trifler? Nothing at all! Not the resemblance of half a little finger. Yet all of them shout at once: The Inspector! the Inspector! Who was it who first gave out he was an official? Answer me!

Char. Com. (*shrugging his shoulders*). It all happened in such a way that I wouldn't tell you, if you were to kill me. Our wits were befogged; it was the devil's doing!

Judge. Who started the idea? Why, there they are, those enterprising young bucks! (*Points to* DOBCHINSKI *and* BOBCHINSKI.)

Bob. I swear it wasn't *I!* I never thought——

Dob. I hadn't the least idea——

Char. Com. Undoubtedly it was *you!*

Post. Why, certainly it was. They ran like mad from the hotel with the news, "He's here! He's come! He pays no money!" A *fine* bird you discovered!

Gov. Of course it was *you,* you gossiping busybodies, you infernal liars!

Char. Com. I wish you had gone to the devil with your inspector and your stories!

Gov. All you do is to run about the town, and meddle with everybody, you confounded chatterboxes, you tittle-tattling scandal-mongers, you short-tailed jackdaws!

Judge. You confounded bunglers!

Dir. of Schools. You dirty nightcaps!

Char. Com. You pot-bellied drivelers!

> (*All crowd up to them threateningly.*)

Bob. Heavens! it wasn't *I;* it was Dobchinski!

Dob. No, Bobchinski, you certainly were the first to——

Bob.   No, I did *not; you* began it!

Enter a POLICE SERGEANT.

Pol. Ser.   The Inspector-General sent by Imperial command has just arrived, and requests your attendance at once. He awaits you at the hotel, gentlemen.

—" The Inspector-General."

Fedor Dostoevski

The Crocodile

ON the 13th of this present month of January, 1865, at half past twelve in the day, Elyona Ivanovna, the spouse of my learned friend, fellow in office, and distant connection, Ivan Matvyeich, desired to visit the crocodile which is now to be seen for a certain price in the Passage, the great St. Petersburg arcade. Ivan Matvyeich, having already in his pocket his ticket for a foreign tour (it was more from curiosity than for his health that he was going abroad), and therefore considering himself as off duty and perfectly free for the whole morning, not only did not oppose his wife's uncontrollable desire, but even became fired with enthusiasm himself. "A splendid idea," he said; "we'll go and see the crocodile. Before starting for Europe it is well to make oneself acquainted with its native population." And with these words he took his wife upon his arm, and instantly started off with her for the Passage. I, as usual, went with them, in my character as family friend. I had never seen Ivan Matvyeich in a more cheerful mood than on that memorable morning. How true it is that we know not our fate beforehand!

The moment we entered the Passage he went into raptures over the magnificence of the building; and when we reached the shop in which the newly arrived monster was on view, he even wished to pay the crocodile-keeper the twenty-five copecks for my admission out of his own pocket—a thing which had never happened with him before. On entering, we found ourselves in a small room, in which, besides the crocodile, were several cockatoos, and a collection of monkeys in a separate cage in the background. To the left hand of the door, by the wall, stood a large tin tank, something like a bath, covered with a strong iron-wire netting, and at the bottom of it were two or three inches of water. In this shallow puddle lay an enormous crocodile, as still as a log, perfectly motionless, and appearing to have lost all his powers in our damp and, for foreigners, inhospitable climate. At first sight the monster aroused no particular interest in any of us.

"So that's the crocodile!" said Elyona Ivanovna regretfully, in a singsong voice. "I thought he would be—quite different, somehow."

She probably expected him to be made of diamonds. The German exhibitor, at once keeper and owner of the crocodile, who had come into the room, looked at us with an air of the greatest pride.

"He's right," whispered Ivan Matvyeich to me; "for he knows that no one else in all Russia is exhibiting a crocodile."

I attributed this utterly senseless remark to the particularly pleasant humor that Ivan Matvyeich was in; for, on the whole, he was a very envious man.

"I think your crocodile is dead," said Elyona Ivanovna, piqued by the ungraciousness of the German, and turning to him with a fascinating smile, intended to "vanquish this boor"—a peculiarly feminine maneuver.

"Oh, no, madam," answered the German in his broken Russian, and, half-lifting the network of the tank, he began to tap the crocodile on the head with a cane.

At this the perfidious monster, to show that it was alive,

slightly moved its feet and tail, raised its head, and uttered a sound resembling a prolonged snuffle.

"There, don't be cross, Karlchen," caressingly said the German, whose vanity was flattered.

"What a horrid brute! I am quite afraid of him," lisped Elyona Ivanovna, still more coquettishly. "I shall dream of him now at night!"

"But he not vill bite you at ze night, madam," gallantly rejoined the German, and burst out laughing at his own joke, though none of us answered him.

"Come, Semyon Semyonich," continued Elyona Ivanovna, addressing herself to me, "let's go and look at the monkeys. I am awfully fond of monkeys; some of them are such little loves; but the crocodile is horrible."

"Oh, don't be afraid, my dear," Ivan Matvyeich called after us, showing off his bravery before his wife. "This sleepy denizen of the realm of the Pharaohs will do us no harm;" and he remained beside the tank. He even took off one glove, and began to tickle the crocodile's nose with it, in the hope, as he afterward confessed, of making it snore again. The keeper, out of politeness to a lady, followed Elyona Ivanovna to the monkeys' cage.

Thus all was well, and there was no sign of coming misfortune. Elyona Ivanovna was so much fascinated with the monkeys that she appeared completely absorbed in them. She uttered screams of delight, talked incessantly to me, as if wishing to ignore the keeper altogether, and went into fits of laughing over resemblances which she found in the monkeys to her most intimate friends and acquaintances. I, too, was greatly amused, for there could be no doubt as to the likeness. The German did not know whether to laugh or not, and therefore ended by scowling. At this moment an appalling, I may even say supernatural, shriek suddenly shook the room. Not knowing what to think, I stood for a moment rooted to the spot; then, hearing Elyona Ivanovna shrieking, too, I turned hastily round; and what did I see! I saw—oh, heavens!—I saw the unhappy Ivan Matvyeich in the fearful jaws of the crocodile, seized across the middle, lifted horizontally in the air, and kicking despairingly. Then —a moment—and he was gone!

I cannot even attempt to describe the agitation of Elyona Ivanovna. After her first cry she stood for some time as petrified, and stared at the scene before her, as if indifferently, though her eyes were starting out of her head; then she suddenly burst into a piercing shriek. I caught her by the hands. At this moment the keeper, who until now had also stood petrified with horror, clasped his hands, and raising his eyes to heaven, cried aloud:

"Oh, my crocodile! Oh, mein allerliebstes Karlchen! Mutter! Mutter! Mutter!"

At this cry the back door opened, and "Mutter," a red-cheeked, untidy, elderly woman in a cap, rushed with a yell toward her son.

Then began an awful tumult. Elyona Ivanovna, beside herself, reiterated one single phrase, "Cut it! Cut it!" and rushed from the keeper to the "Mutter," and back to the keeper, imploring them (evidently in a fit of frenzy) to "cut" something or some one for some reason. Neither the keeper nor "Mutter" took any notice of either of us; they were hanging over the tank, and shrieking like stuck pigs.

"He is gone dead; he vill sogleich burst, because he von ganz official of der government eat up haf!" cried the keeper.

"Unser Karlchen, unser allerliebstes Karlchen wird sterben!" wailed the mother.

"Ve are orphans, vitout bread!" moaned the keeper.

"Cut it! Cut it! Cut it open!" screamed Elyona Ivanovna, hanging on to the German's coat.

"He did teaze ze crocodile! Vy your man teaze ze crocodile?" yelled the German, wriggling away. "You vill pay me if Karlchen wird bersten! Das war mein Sohn, das war mein einziger Sohn!"

"Cut it!" shrieked Elyona Ivanovna.

"How! You vill dat my crocodile shall be die? No, your man shall be die first, and denn my crocodile. Mein Vater show von crocodile, mein Grossvater show von crocodile, mein Sohn shall show von crocodile, and I shall show von crocodile. All ve shall show crocodile. I am ganz Europa famous, and you are not ganz Europa famous, and you do be me von fine pay shall!"

"Ja, ja!" agreed the woman savagely; "ve you not let out; fine ven Karlchen vill bersten."

"For that matter," I put in calmly, in the hope of getting Elyona Ivanovna home without further ado, "there's no use in cutting it open, for in all probability our dear Ivan Matvyeich is now soaring in the empyrean."

"My dear," remarked at this moment the voice of Ivan Matvyeich, with startling suddenness, "my advice, my dear, is to act through the bureau of police, for the German will not comprehend the truth without the assistance of the police."

These words, uttered with firmness and gravity, and expressing astonishing presence of mind, at first so much amazed us that we could not believe our ears. Of course, however, we instantly ran to the crocodile's tank and listened to the speech of the unfortunate captive with a mixture of reverence and distrust. His voice sounded muffled, thin, and even squeaky, as though coming from a long distance.

"Ivan Matvyeich, my dearest, are you alive?" lisped Elyona Ivanovna.

"Alive and well," answered Ivan Matvyeich; "and, thanks to the Almighty, swallowed whole without injury. I am only disturbed by doubt as to how the superior authorities will regard this episode; for, after having taken a ticket to go abroad, to go into a crocodile instead is hardly sensible."

"Oh, my dear, don't worry about sense now; first of all we must somehow or other dig you out," interrupted Elyona Ivanovna.

"Tig!" cried the German. "I not vill let you to tig ze crocodile! Now shall bery mush Publikum be come, and I shall fifety copeck take, and Karlchen shall leave off to burst."

"Gott sei Dank!" added the mother.

"They are right," calmly remarked Ivan Matvyeich; "the economic principle before everything."

"Dear friend," I exclaimed, "I will fly at once to the authorities and complain, for I feel convinced that we can't settle this mess by ourselves!"

"I also am of that opinion," said Ivan Matvyeich; "but without economic compensation it is hard, in our age of financial crisis, to rip open the belly of a crocodile, and, nevertheless, we are confronted with the inevitable question: What will the owner take for his crocodile? With this there is also another question: Who is to pay? For you know I have not the means."

"Couldn't you get your salary in advance?" I began timidly. But the German instantly interrupted:

"I not sell ze crocodile. I tree tausend sell ze crocodile,

Fedor Dostoevski

I four tausend sell ze crocodile! Now shall mush Publikum come. I fife tausend sell ze crocodile!"

In a word, he carried it with a high hand; avarice and greed shone triumphantly in his eyes.

"I will go!" I cried indignantly.

"And I! And I too! I will go to Andrey Osipich himself. I will move him with my tears!" wailed Elyona Ivanovna.

"Don't do that, my dear," hastily interrupted Ivan Matvyeich, who had long been jealous of Andrey Osipich's admiration of his wife, and knew that she was glad of a chance to weep before a man of refinement, as tears became her very well. "And you, my friend," he continued, addressing me, "you had better go to Timofei Semyonich. And now take away Elyona Ivanovna. Be calm, my love," he added to her. "I am tired of all this noise and feminine quarreling, and wish to take a little nap. It is warm and soft here, though I have not yet had time to look about me in this unexpected refuge."

"Look about you! Is there any light there?" cried Elyona Ivanovna in rapture.

"I am surrounded by impenetrable darkness," answered the poor captive; "but I can feel, and, so to say, look about me with my hands. Good-by! Be calm, and do not deny yourself recreation. You, Semyon Semyonich, come back to me this evening, and, as you are absent-minded and may forget, tie a knot in your handkerchief." . . .

The respectable Timofei Semyonich received me in a hurried and, as it were, somewhat embarrassed manner.

He evidently knew all, much to my astonishment. However, I told him the whole story over again, with all details. I spoke with emotion, for at that moment I was fulfilling

57

the duty of a true friend. He listened without any great surprise, but with evident suspiciousness.

"Just imagine," he said, when I had done; "I always expected that this very thing would happen to him."

"But why, Timofei Semyonich? The case is a most exceptional one."

"Certainly. But during the whole term of his service Ivan Matvyeich has been leading up to this result. He's too nimble—yes, and too conceited. Always 'progress' and new-fangled ideas—and that's where progress ends."

"But advise us," said I; "guide us, as a man of experience —as a relative! What shall we do? Go to the authorities, or——"

"To the authorities? On no account!" hastily exclaimed Timofei Semyonich. "If you want my advice, I say the first thing is to hush up the matter, and act in the character of a private person. It is a suspicious case, an unheard-of case. The worst is that it's unheard of—there's no precedent; indeed, it looks very bad. So that the first of all things is caution. Let him stop where he is a bit. He must have patience, patience!"

"But how can he stop there, Timofei Semyonich? Supposing he chokes to death?"

"Why should he? Didn't you tell me that he had made rather a comfortable arrangement for himself there?"

I repeated all over again. Timofei Semyonich meditated.

"Hm!" he pronounced, holding his snuff-box in his hands. "In my opinion it will be even a very good thing for him to stop there a bit, instead of going abroad. He can think at his leisure; of course it wouldn't do to choke, and he must take measures for the preservation of his health— I mean, he must take care not to get a cough or anything. As for the German, my personal opinion is that he is right—more so than the other side, indeed; because, you see, Ivan Matvyeich got into *his* crocodile without leave, and not *he* into Ivan Matvyeich's crocodile; indeed, so far as I remember, Ivan Matvyeich had no crocodile of his own. Very well, then, a crocodile constitutes private property, therefore without remuneration it cannot be cut open, as I take it."

"To save a human life, Timofei Semyonich?"

"Oh, well, that's the business of the police. You should apply to them."

"But then, again, Ivan Matvyeich may be needed. He may be sent for——"

"Ivan Matvyeich needed? Ha-ha-ha! Besides, he is supposed to be on furlough; therefore we can ignore the whole matter and suppose him to be looking at European countries. It will be another case if he doesn't turn up at the end of his furlough; then, of course, we must make inquiries."

"Three months! Timofei Semyonich, for mercy's sake!"

"It's his own fault. Who asked him to poke his nose in there? I suppose next there'll have to be a nurse-maid hired for him at government expense, and that's not allowed in the regulations, you know. But the main point is that the crocodile is property; therefore what is called the economic principle comes into play. And the economic principle is before everything. Now, the day before yesterday, at Luka Andreich's evening, Ignatyi Prokofich was talking about that. He's a capitalist, a business man, and he put it all so plainly, you know. 'What we want,' he said, 'is industry; we have too little industry. It must be created. We must create capital; that is, we must create a middle class; we must create what is called a *bourgeoisie*. And as

we have no capital, we must import it from abroad.' As you
see, we are making efforts to attract foreign capital into the
country, and now judge for yourself: the capital of the
crocodile-keeper (a foreigner attracted here) has barely had
time to become doubled by means of Ivan Matvyeich, and
we, instead of protecting the foreign possessor of property,
are aiming, on the contrary, to rip open the belly of the
fundamental capital itself! Now, really, is that consistent?
In my opinion, Ivan Matvyeich, as a true son of the Fatherland, should even be glad and proud that, by the addition of
himself, he has doubled, and maybe trebled, the value of the
foreign crocodile. That, sir, is an essential feature in the
attracting of capital. If one succeeds, perhaps another will
come with a crocodile, and a third will bring two or three at
once, and capital will collect round them. And so you get
your *bourgeoisie*. People must be encouraged, my good
sir."

"But, Timofei Semyonich," I exclaimed, "you demand almost supernatural self-abnegation of poor Ivan Matvyeich!"

"And who told him to get into the crocodile? A respectable man, a man holding a certain position, living in lawful
wedlock, and suddenly—such a step! Now, *is* that consistent?"

"But the step was taken unintentionally."

"How should I know that? And then, how is the crocodile-keeper to be paid, eh? No, no, he had better stop where
he is; he has nowhere to hurry to."

A happy thought flashed into my mind.

"Can't we manage it this way?" said I. "If he is fated to
stay in the entrails of the monster, and if, by the will of
Providence, he remains alive, can't he send in a petition that
he shall be regarded as serving during his sojourn there?"

"Hm—you mean, as on furlough, without salary?"

"No, I mean with his salary."

"On what ground?"

"As being on an expedition, on government service——"

"What expedition? Where to?"

"Why, into the entrails—the crocodile's entrails—so to say, to collect information, to study facts on the spot. Of course it is a new idea, but then it is progressive, and at the same time it shows an interest in education."

Timofei Semyonich meditated.

"To despatch an official," he remarked at last, "into a crocodile's entrails on a special commission, is, according to my personal opinion, absurd. It is not provided for by the regulations. And then, what investigation can there be to make there?"

"Well, you know, natural philosophy—I mean the study of nature on the spot, in the living organism. Natural science is all the rage now, and botany and all that. He could live there and give information—well, for instance, about the digestion—or even the general habits—for the sake of obtaining facts."

"This would belong to the department of statistics. Well, I'm not strong on that point, and then I'm not a philosopher. You say 'facts.' As it is, we're crowded with facts, and don't know what to do with them all. And then, these statistics are dangerous things."

"How so?"

"Very dangerous. And, moreover, you must admit that he will have to communicate his facts while lying down at his ease. How can a man be on government service while he's lying down? That, again, is an innovation, and a dangerous one; and for that, too, there is no precedent. Now, if there were even *any* sort of precedent, then, in my opinion, it might be possible to arrange a commission."

"But up till now live crocodiles have not been brought here, Timofei Semyonich."

"Hm—yes." He meditated again. "There is some truth in your argument, and it might even serve as a basis for the further development of the case. But again, on the other hand, if, with the introduction of live crocodiles, government servants begin to disappear, and then, in consideration of the fact that it is soft and warm inside there, they want to be on commissions in order to live there, and then spend their time lying down, you must acknowledge it'll be a bad example. Yes, every one will be trying to get paid for doing nothing. Well, good-by. Are you coming?"

"No, I must go back to the captive."

"Ah, yes, to the captive. Oh-h-h! That's what frivolity leads to!" . . .

When I reached the passage it was about nine o'clock, and I had to enter the crocodile-room by the back door, for the German had shut up his place earlier than usual. He was walking about at his ease in a greasy old coat, and was evidently three times more self-satisfied even than in the morning. It was plain that he was troubled with no fears, and that " bery mush Publikum " had come. "Mutter" came out, too, evidently for the purpose of keeping a watch upon me. She and her son often whispered together. Although the premises were shut up, the German took twenty-five copecks as entrance-fee from me. That seems to me an excess of accuracy!

"You vill pay ebery time; ze Publikum vill pay von ruble, and you vill pay twenti-fife copeck, vy for you are von goot friend ob your goot friend, and I honor ze friend."

Fedor Dostoevski

"Is he alive? Is my learned friend alive?" I cried loudly, approaching the crocodile.

"Alive and well," answered Ivan Matvyeich, as if from a distance; "but of that afterward. What news?"

Pretending not to hear the question, I began hastily and with sympathy to put questions in my turn. I asked him how he was, how he got on in the crocodile, and what the inside of a crocodile was like. But he interrupted me irritably.

"What news?" he shouted, in his squeaky voice, which sounded now peculiarly unpleasant.

I related to him all my conversation with Timofei Semyonich, to the minutest detail. In relating it I tried to express that I was somewhat hurt.

"The old man is right," said Ivan Matvyeich. "I like practical people, and can't bear sentimental milksops. Sit down anywhere—on the floor, if you like—and listen to me:

"Now, for the first time, I have leisure to think out how to improve the lot of all humanity. Out of the crocodile shall come forth light and truth. I shall invent a new theory, all my own, of new economic relations—a theory of which I can be proud. Up till now my time has been occupied with the government service and with worldly, frivolous amusements. I shall overthrow everything and become a new Fourier. But to the point: where is my wife?"

I told him how I had left Elyona Ivanovna; but he did not even hear me out.

"I build great hopes upon her," he said. "From next week she must begin to throw open her drawing-room every evening. I feel sure that the keeper will sometimes bring me, together with the crocodile, into my wife's brilliant

63

salon. I will stand, in my tank, in the splendid reception-room and shower around me witty sayings, which I will think out beforehand, in the mornings. I will confide my projects to statesmen; with poets I will speak of verse; with the ladies I will be amusing and fascinating, though strictly moral, and I shall have the advantage of being quite innocuous to their husbands. To the rest of society I will serve as an example of submission to fate and to the will of Providence."

I confess that, though all this was something in Ivan Matvyeich's usual style, it came into my head that he was feverish and light-headed. This was the ordinary, every-day Ivan Matvyeich twenty times magnified.

"My friend," I asked him, "do you hope for a long life? Tell me about yourself: are you well? How do you eat, sleep, and breathe? I am your friend, and indeed you must acknowledge that the case is altogether supernatural, therefore my curiosity is altogether natural."

"Idle curiosity, and nothing more," he answered sententiously. "But you shall be satisfied. You ask, How am I domiciled in the entrails of the monster? In the first place, the crocodile, to my great surprise, turns out to be completely hollow. Its interior consists of what appears to be an enormous empty sac, made of gutta-percha. If it were not so, think yourself, how could I find room in it?"

"Is it possible?" I exclaimed in utter stupefaction. "Can the crocodile really be quite empty?"

"Quite," severely and dogmatically affirmed Ivan Matvyeich. "In all probability it is so constructed in accordance with the laws of Nature herself. The crocodile has only jaws, furnished with sharp teeth, and, in addition to the jaws, a rather long tail; and in reality that is all. In the middle, between these two extremities, is an empty space, enclosed in something which resembles india-rubber, and which, in all probability, is india-rubber."

"But the ribs, the stomach, the intestines, the liver, the heart?" I interrupted almost crossly.

"There is nothing, absolutely no-th-thing of the kind, and probably there never was anything of the kind. All those things are the idle fancies of frivolous travelers. Just as you swell out an air-cushion with air, so I now swell out the crocodile with my person. It is elastic to an incredible degree. For that matter, this hollow formation of the crocodile is fully in accordance with natural science. For supposing, for instance, you were commissioned to construct a new crocodile, the question would naturally present itself to you, What is the fundamental characteristic of the crocodile? The answer is plain, To swallow people. How should this aim—the swallowing of people—be attained in the construction of the crocodile? The answer is still plainer, Make him hollow. The science of physics has long proved that Nature abhors a vacuum. According to this law, the interior of the crocodile must necessarily be empty, in order that the crocodile may abhor a vacuum and may therefore swallow everything that comes to hand, so as to fill itself up. And this is the only reasonable cause that all crocodiles eat men. Now, the construction of man is different: for instance, the emptier a human head, the less desire it feels to fill itself up; and this is the only exception to the general rule. All this has now become as clear as day to me; all this I have comprehended out of my own intellect and experience, being, as it were, in the entrails of Nature, in Nature's retort, listening to the beating of her pulse. Even etymology agrees with my theory, for the very name of the crocodile implies devouring greed. Crocodile, *coccodrillo,* is an Italian word—a word contemporary, it may be, with the ancient Egyptian Pharaohs, and evidently derived from the French root, *croquer,* which means, to eat, to devour, or in any way to use any object for food. All this I intend to explain in my first lecture to the audience which will assemble in Elyona Ivanovna's *salon,* when I am carried there in my tank."

" My dear friend, don't you think you had better take a— a cooling medicine?" I involuntarily exclaimed. " He's delirious, delirious! " I repeated to myself in horror.

" Fiddlesticks! " he replied contemptuously. " Moreover, in my present position that would be not altogether convenient. For that matter, I knew you would begin to talk about cooling medicines."

" Ivan Matvyeich," said I, " it is hard to believe all the wonders you speak of. And do you mean to tell me that you really, really intend never to dine any more? "

" What silly things you think about, you frivolous rattle-pate! I tell you of great ideas, and you— Let me tell you, then, that I am sufficiently nourished with the great ideas that illumine the night which surrounds me. For the rest, the good-natured keeper of the monster has talked the matter over with his kind-hearted mother, and they have decided together that every morning they will introduce into the jaws of the crocodile a curved metallic tube, something like a shepherd's pipe, through which I am to suck coffee or broth with white bread soaked in it. The tube has already been ordered from a neighboring shop, but I consider that this is superfluous luxury. I hope to live at least a thousand years, if it be true that crocodiles live so long. By the bye, you had better look that up to-morrow in some book on natural history and let me know, for I may have made a mistake and confused the crocodile with some other fossil. One consideration alone somewhat disturbs me. As I am dressed in cloth and have boots on my feet, the crocodile is, of course, unable to digest me. Moreover, I am alive, and resist the digesting of myself with all my force of will; for, naturally, I do not wish to turn into what all food turns into, as that would be too humiliating. But I fear one thing: in the course of a thousand years the cloth of my coat, which, unfortunately, is of Russian manufacture, may decay, and I, remaining without clothes, may then, notwithstanding all my indignation, begin to be digested; and although by day I shall not permit, shall not under any circumstances allow this, by night, in sleep, when a man is deprived of his free-will, I may be overtaken by the most humiliating doom of a mere potato, pancake, or slice of veal. The thought of this drives me to frenzy. If only on this ground, the revenue law must be changed in order to encourage the importation of English cloth, which is stronger, and therefore will resist Nature longer in cases of persons tumbling into crocodiles. I shall take the earliest opportunity of communicating this idea to some statesman, and also to the political critics of our St. Petersburg daily papers. They can cry it up. I hope that this will not be the only idea they will take from me. I foresee that every morning a whole assembly of them, armed with editorial twenty-five-copeck pieces, will crowd around me, to catch my thoughts upon the telegrams of the day before. In short, the future appears to me in quite a rose-colored light."

"High fever! High fever!" I whispered to myself. "But, my friend, what about liberty?" I asked, wishing to hear all he had to say upon that point. "You see, you are, as it were, in a dungeon, whereas man should enjoy freedom."

"You are dull," he replied. "Savages care for independence, but wise men love only order, and there is no order——"

"Ivan Matvyeich, for mercy's sake!"

"Silence! Listen!" he screamed out in his rage at being interrupted. "My spirit has never soared so high as now. In my narrow retreat I have but one fear: the literary criticism of the big magazines, and the gibes of our satirical papers. I fear that frivolous visitors, fools, envious persons, and nihilists generally, may hold me up to ridicule. But I will take measures. I await with impatience to-morrow's expression of public opinion, and, above all, the criticisms in the newspapers. Be sure and tell me about the papers to-morrow. But enough; you are probably sleepy. Go home, and don't think of what I said about criticism. I am not afraid of criticism, for it is in a critical position itself. It is sufficient to be wise and virtuous, and you are certain to be raised upon a pedestal. If you do not become Socrates, you will become Diogenes, or perhaps both at once, and that is my future theory as regards humanity." . . . .

At the department I, of course, made no sign that I was devoured with such cares and responsibilities. I soon observed, though, that several of the most progressive daily papers were on that morning passing unusually quickly from hand to hand among my fellow officials, who read them with exceedingly grave faces. The first which fell into my hands was the *Listok,* a paper without any special tendency, but on the whole very humanitarian—for which it was generally despised in our set, although much read. It was with a certain surprise that I read the following:

"Yesterday our great capital was filled with extraordinary

rumors. A certain N., a well-known gormand of the highest spheres of society, wearied, no doubt, of the *cuisine* of our first-class restaurants, entered the building of the Passage at that part where an immense crocodile, just brought to the capital, was on view, and demanded that the latter should be prepared for his dinner. After bargaining with the keeper, he instantly set to work to devour him (that is, not the keeper, an exceedingly peaceable German with a taste for accuracy, but the crocodile) alive, cutting off juicy morsels with a penknife and gulping them down with extraordinary speed. Gradually the whole of the crocodile disappeared into his fat paunch, and he even set to work upon the ichneumon, the constant companion of the crocodile, probably supposing that would be equally delicious. We have no objection to this new product, already long familiar to foreign gastronomists. We have even prophesied its introduction. In Egypt the English lords and travelers go out in regular parties to catch the crocodile, and eat the monster's back in the form of steak, with mustard, onions, and potatoes. The French followers of de Lesseps prefer the feet, baked in hot ashes, though, indeed, they do this merely to spite the English, who make fun of them. Here both dishes will probably be appreciated. We, for our part, gladly welcome this new branch of industry, of which our great and active fatherland is so much in want. After the disappearance of this first crocodile into the interior of a St. Petersburg gormand, it is probable that, before a year passes, they will be imported by hundreds. And why should crocodiles not be acclimatized here in Russia? If the water of the Neva is too cold for these interesting foreigners, we have reservoirs within the capital and streams and lakes without. Why, for instance, should crocodiles not be reared at Pargolov or Pavlovsk, or in Moscow, in the Priessnensky or the Samotyok ponds? While providing a delicate and wholesome food for our refined gastronomists, they would also afford amusement to the ladies strolling past these ponds, and would serve for our children as a lesson in natural history. The skin of the crocodiles could be made into portfolios, traveling-trunks, cigarette-cases, and pocketbooks, and perhaps many a thousand rubles—in the greasy notes for which our commercial classes have so strong a predilection—would find their way into crocodile-skins. We hope to return often to this interesting subject."

Nikolai Nekrasov

A Moral Man

A STRICTLY moral man have I been ever,
And never injured anybody—never.
I lent my friend a sum he could not pay;
I jogged his memory in a friendly way,
Then took the law of him th' affair to end;
The law to prison sent my worthy friend.
He died there—not a farthing for poor me!
I am not angry, though I've cause to be;
His debt that very moment I forgave,
And shed sad tears of sorrow o'er his grave.
A strictly moral man have I been ever,
And never injured anybody—never.

I sent a serf of mine to learn the dressing
Of meat. He learned it—a good cook's a blessing—
But strangely did neglect his occupation,
And gained a taste not suited to his station:
He liked to read, to reason, to discuss.
I, tired of scolding, without further fuss
Had the rogue flogged—all for the love of him.
He went and drowned himself—what a strange whim!
A strictly moral man have I been ever,
And never injured anybody—never.

My silly daughter fell in love, one day,
And with a tutor wished to run away.

I threatened curses, and pronounced my ban;
She yielded, and espoused a rich old man.
Their house was splendid, brimming o'er with wealth,
But suddenly the poor child lost her health,
And in a year consumption wrought her doom;
She left us mourning o'er her early tomb.
A strictly moral man have I been ever,
And never injured anybody—never.

The Soldier

Then up there comes a veteran,
  With medals on his breast;
He scarcely lives, but yet he strives
  To drink with all the rest.
"A lucky man am I!" he cries,
And thus to prove the fact he tries:
"In what consists a soldier's luck?
  Pray, listen while I tell:
In twenty fights or more I've been,
  And yet I never fell;
And, what is more, in peaceful times
  Full health I never knew.
Yet, all the same, I have contrived
  Not to give Death his due.
Also, for sins both great and small,
  Full many a time they've me
With sticks unmercifully flogged;
  Yet I'm alive, you see!"
          —"Who Lives Happily in Russia?"

72

Ivan Turgeniev

Russians Abroad

In front of the Conversation House at Baden-Baden the usual crowd was assembled. The band was playing the old, well-known tunes in the pavilion. Round about the green tables, indoors, were to be seen the customary faces, with that expression of dull, savage, grasping cupidity which the habit of gambling will at last stamp upon the finest features. And, as usual, there was the inevitable gathering of our worthy compatriots near the Russian Tree. On meeting, they bowed to one another with the dignified coolness proper to persons of the highest social standing. When they had sat down, they did not talk to each other, but tried to kill time by doing nothing at all, or by laughing at the silly, stale, vulgar jokes of a so-called Bohemian, who came from Paris, a loquacious buffoon with an absurd little peak of hair on his chin, and enormous boots on his flat feet. These jokes of his, which he had borrowed from old Parisian comic papers, were loudly applauded by the Russian nobility, who showed that they appreciated foreign wit while acknowledging their own want of imagination.

The said listening Russians were the flower of our society, the most refined and cultured people of our land. There was Count X., the distinguished amateur, who, though he read like a schoolboy, sang operatic airs superbly—something like a French hair-dresser. There was the fascinating Baron Y., incomparably versatile, author, orator statesman, and scholar.

73

And then there was Prince Z., a patron of the masses and the Church, who had made a fortune out of the manufacture of adulterated brandy. And there was the dashing General O., who had once upon a time gained a great victory, somewhere, over somebody, but whose want of self-mastery was evident through his behavior. A delightful fellow was P., an alleged invalid and wit, who was in reality as strong as an ox and as stupid as an owl, and whose specialty was elegant deportment. Statesmen and diplomats of European fame there were, profound and acute, who thought that Irish bulls were issued by the pope, and that the taxes for the support of the poor were contributed by the poor themselves. Besides all these were the ardent but diffident adherents of the stage, young bloods with hair exquisitely parted behind, gorgeous whiskers, and clothes made in London.

Yet, though there seemed nothing wanting to put these gentlemen on an equal footing with the buffoon from Paris, our ladies nevertheless paid no attention to them. Thus, Countess C., the renowned lady of fashion, from her malicious tongue nicknamed " Queen of the Wasps," when the buffoon was absent slighted her countrymen, showing her preference for Italians, Austrians, Americans, *attachés* of foreign legations, and even the greenest sprigs of the German aristocracy. About this social star hovered Princess Babette, in whose arms Chopin had breathed his last—an honor claimed by a thousand ladies in Europe; Princess Annette, who would have been a fairy but for her stoutness— qualifying her for a washerwoman; Princess Paquette, whose husband, after being made governor of his province, had got into a fisticuff match with a subordinate, and then absconded with twenty thousand rubles of government funds; and finally there might be mentioned giddy Mlle. Zizi and melancholy Mlle. Zozo. But, one and all, these ladies turned their backs upon their countrymen in cold disdain.—*" Smoke."*

Beneficence and Gratitude

ONE day the Supreme Being took it into His head to give a great banquet in His azure palace.

All the virtues were invited. Men He did not ask—only ladies.

There was a large number of them, great and small. The lesser virtues were more agreeable and genial than the great ones; but they all appeared to be in good-humor, and chatted amiably together, as was only becoming for near relations and friends.

But the Supreme Being noticed two charming ladies who seemed to be totally unacquainted.

The Host gave one of the ladies His arm, and led her up to the other.

" Beneficence ! " He said, indicating the first.

" Gratitude ! " He added, indicating the second.

Both the virtues were amazed beyond expression. Ever since the world had stood—and it had been standing a long time—this was the first time they had met.

—*" Poems in Prose."*

Prayer

WHATEVER a man prays for, he prays for a miracle. Every prayer reduces itself to this: " Great God, grant that twice two be not four."

Only such a prayer is a real prayer from person to person. To pray to the Cosmic Spirit, to the Higher Being, to the Kantian, the Hegelian, quintessential, formless God, is impossible and unthinkable.

But can even a personal, living, imaged God make twice two not to be four?

Every believer is bound to answer " He can," and is bound to persuade himself of it.

But what if reason sets him revolting against his unreasonableness?

Then Shakespeare comes to his aid: " There are more things in heaven and earth, Horatio," etc.

And if they set about confuting him in the name of truth, he has but to repeat the famous question: " What is truth? "

And so let us eat, drink, and be merry—and say our prayers.—*" Poems in Prose."*

The Fool

ONCE upon a time there was a fool.

For a long period he lived in peace and contentment; but by degrees rumors began to reach him that he was regarded on all sides as a common idiot.

The fool was abashed, and began to ponder gloomily how he might put an end to these unpleasant rumors.

A sudden idea at last illuminated his dull little brain. Without the slightest delay he put it into practise.

A friend met him in the street, and fell to praising a well-known painter.

" Upon my word," cried the fool, " that painter has been

out of date for years! You didn't know it? I should never have suspected it of you! You are quite behind the times."

The friend was alarmed, and promptly agreed with the fool.

"Such a splendid book I read yesterday!" said another friend to him.

"Upon my word," cried the fool, "I wonder you're not ashamed! The book's good for nothing; every one has seen through it long ago. Didn't you know it? You're quite behind the times."

This friend, too, was alarmed, and he agreed with the fool.

"What a wonderful fellow my friend N—— is!" said a third friend to the fool. "Now, there's a really fine man for you!"

"Upon my word!" cried the fool. "N——, the notorious scoundrel! He swindled all his relations. Every one knows that. You're quite behind the times."

The third friend was alarmed, and he agreed with the fool and deserted his friend. And whoever and whatever was praised in the fool's presence, he had the same retort for everything.

Sometimes he would add reproachfully, "And do you still believe in authorities?"

"Spiteful! Malignant!" his friends began to say of the fool. "But what a brain! And what a tongue!" Others would add, "Oh, yes, he is very talented."

It ended in an editor of a paper proposing to the fool that he should undertake the reviewing column.

And the fool fell to criticizing everything and every one, without in the least changing his manner or his exclamations.

Now he who once declaimed against authorities is himself an authority, and the young men venerate him and fear him.

And what else can they do, poor young men? Though one ought not, as a general rule, to venerate anybody, in this case, if one didn't venerate him, one would find oneself quite behind the times!

Fools succeed well among cowards.—*"Poems in Prose."*

Mikhail Saltykov—"Shchedrin"

Two Generals and a Peasant

SOME years ago there lived in St. Petersburg two generals. Now these generals had grown old in the service of the government, having spent the whole of their lives in small civil offices, and consequently they knew nothing beyond the mere routine of their duties. Their entire vocabulary consisted of such words as "I remain, sir, most respectfully yours." In due time the generals retired on a pension, each hired a cook, and they settled down in Redtape Avenue to a comfortable old age.

One morning, when they awoke, they found themselves lying together in a single bed.

"I had a horrible dream last night, your Excellency," said one of the generals. "I actually thought I was living on a desert island."

Hardly had the words left his mouth, when he sprang out of bed, followed by the other general.

"Good heavens! what can this mean? Where are we?" they exclaimed in unison.

Then they began to pinch each other, convinced that they must still be asleep. But they could not, try as they might, persuade themselves that they were dreaming. Except for a small patch of land to the rear of them, they were surrounded by the wide sea. For the first time since they had left their desks the generals began to weep. When they looked at each other they discovered that they were clothed only in nightgowns. On the neck of each, however, hung a medal.

79

" How I should like a cup of coffee! " said one general. But when he remembered his sad plight, he again burst into tears.

" What is to be done? " he went on, still sobbing. " It would do no good to write a report about it."

" Listen to me," said the other general. " You go toward the east, and I will go toward the west, and at nightfall we will return to this spot. That may be the means of our discovering something."

But they did not know in which direction east or west lay. They remembered that a higher official had once told them that to find the east you must stand with your face toward the north, and then turn to the right. They began, therefore, to look for the north, and in doing so placed themselves in every position imaginable, but as the horizon of their experience was bounded by the government office, they came to no conclusion.

" You go to the right, and I will go to the left; that will come to the same thing," said one of the generals, who at one time had taught handwriting in a boys' school, and consequently possessed a little common sense.

The general who went to the right saw fruit-trees growing, but when he tried to get an apple he found that the fruit hung beyond his reach. When he tried to climb for it he tore his clothes to pieces, but accomplished nothing else. Soon after this the general came to a stream, which was as full of fish as the fish-shop on the Fontanka Canal. " If only those fish were cooked! " said the general to himself, quite faint with hunger. In a wood he saw partridges, woodcock, and hares, but there was no way of catching any of them for food, and so he had to return empty-handed to the place of departure. The other general was already there.

Mikhail Saltykov

"Well, your Excellency, what luck?"

"I have found an old copy of the *Moscow Gazette,* but nothing else."

The generals lay down again and tried to sleep, but hunger kept them awake, and they were also concerned as to the fate of their pensions.

"Who would ever have guessed, your Excellency, that food in its first stage swims, flies, and grows on trees?" said one general, thinking of the fish, fruit, and birds he had seen. "Therefore, when one wants to eat a pheasant, one must first catch it, kill it, pluck it, and cook it. But how is all that to be done?"

"Yes, how is that to be done?" repeated the other general. "It almost seems to me that I could eat my boots, I am so hungry!"

"Gloves would not be so bad, either," said the other general, "especially when they have been worn some time."

Suddenly the generals looked at each other; their eyes flashed fire, their teeth clinched, guttural sounds burst from their lips. In a second they were fighting furiously. The air was filled with groans and flying hair. The general who had been a writing-master got his teeth into his opponent's medal and accidentally swallowed it. The sight of blood brought them to their senses.

"Saints of heaven, defend us!" they exclaimed with one accord. "We shall eat each other next!"

"But how did we get here? What imp of malevolence has been tricking us?"

"We must think of something more pleasant, your Excellency, or murder will be done," said the other general. "What do you say to this, for instance: Why does the sun set before rising, instead of *vice versa?*"

"What a silly question! Didn't you rise first yourself, go to the office, write, and finally retire?"

"But why not the other way about? First I go to bed, dream various things, and afterward rise."

"Perhaps; but when I served the government I always thought of it as beginning with the morning, then dinner, and then bed."

But the mention of dinner cut the conversation off short by recalling their pangs of hunger.

"I once heard a doctor say that a man can live for many days on his natural juices," began one of the generals.

"Really?"

"Yes. It seems that one juice develops another, which, in turn, is consumed, until finally none is left."

"And then?"

"Then one must eat something."

In fact, no matter what the generals started to talk about, the discussion ended in food, and this only tended to still further inflame their appetites. They decided to stop talking, and, remembering the copy of the *Moscow Gazette* which they had found, they turned to it for amusement.

"Yesterday," read one general with a quavering voice, "the governor of our historic capital held a great banquet, to which one hundred guests were invited. The epicures of the world seemed to have united to provide this wonderful feast. Royal pheasants from the Caucasus, caviare fresh from the banks of the Caspian, and even strawberries, which are almost unknown in our city in the month of Feb-ruary——"

"Merciful heavens! is there no other subject in the world?" exclaimed the other general in despair; and, taking the newspaper from his colleague's hand, he read:

Mikhail Saltykov

"A correspondent writes from Tula: 'A dinner was held yesterday to celebrate the capture of a sturgeon from the river Upa. The fish in question was brought in on an enormous wooden tray, buried in cucumbers and crowned with a sprig of green. Dr. R., who presided on the occasion, took special pains to see that each of the guests received his share. The sauce was tasty in the extreme——' "

"My dear Excellency, it seems that you also are partial in your reading!" broke in the first general, and retaking the paper, he read:

"A correspondent writes us from Viatka: 'An old fisherman has invented the following interesting recipe for fish broth: Take a live turbot and beat him with a stick until his liver becomes swollen with fury; then——' "

This was too much for the generals. Even their own thoughts played them traitor. But suddenly the general who had taught handwriting was seized with an idea.

"What do you say, your Excellency, to our looking for a peasant, an ordinary peasant? He would undoubtedly be able to give us fresh rolls, and catch pheasants and fish for us."

"All very well, but where do you propose to find this peasant?"

"Oh, that will be easy enough. There are peasants everywhere. There must be one on this island, and all we have to do is to find him. He is probably in hiding somewhere because he is too lazy to work."

This scheme pleased the generals so much that they immediately sprang up and set out on their quest. After searching for a long time without success, the smell of stale food attracted them to a tree under which a huge peasant lay sleeping, evidently skulking in the most scandalous fashion. The generals became white with anger, and jerked the man to his feet.

"What, sleeping! And two generals who have had nothing to eat for two days! Get to work this very instant!"

The man looked as if he would have liked to escape, but there was no mistaking the wrath of the two generals.

For a beginning he climbed one of the trees and picked a dozen of the best apples for the generals, reserving an unripe one for himself. Then he scraped the ground, and brought out potatoes. Then he made a fire by rubbing sticks together. Then he made a trap from his own hair, and snared a partridge. Finally, he cooked the provisions so well that the idea even struck the generals they might possibly give the lazy vagabond a bit for himself. They had already forgotten that they had been nearly starved the day before, and they were filled with pride at being generals, who always rose superior to circumstances.

"Now are you content, generals?" asked the lazy peasant.

"We are satisfied with your efforts, dear friend," replied the generals.

"May I not rest a little, then?"

"Certainly, my good man; but first make us a rope."

The peasant at once collected a quantity of wild hemp, soaked it, plaited it, and by nightfall the rope was made. This rope served the generals to such good purpose that they tied the peasant to a tree, so that he might not escape, after which they lay down to sleep.

Day after day passed. The peasant became so expert that he was soon able to cook soup in the palm of his hand. The generals became cheerful, fat, and healthy. They began to realize the fact that they were living on the fat of the land while their pensions were piling up in St. Petersburg.

Mikhail Saltykov

"What is your opinion of the Tower of Babel, your Excellency?" one general would say to the other as they were eating breakfast. "Do you think it was true, or merely a legend?"

"It certainly must have been true. How, otherwise, do you account for the existence of so many languages?"

"Then the flood must also have taken place?"

"Of course it did. Do we not know of the existence of many antediluvian animals? Why, I have even read it in the *Moscow Gazette.*"

"Let us read the *Moscow Gazette,* then."

And they would get the old copy, sit in the shade, and read it through from beginning to end—read of what people had been eating in Moscow, Tula, and other places—and it did not affect them in the least; certainly it did not excite them to envy.

But finally the generals wearied of the monotony of their lives. They thought more and more of the cooks they had left in Redtape Avenue, and occasionally they even wept in secret.

"What do you think they are doing now in Redtape Avenue, your Excellency?" asked one general of the other.

"Please do not mention it, your Excellency!" replied the other. "My heart is yearning for the old days!"

"It is very comfortable here—very comfortable. We cannot complain. And yet it is rather tiresome to be alone, is it not? And then, I regret my uniform."

"Of course you do! Especially as it is one of the fourth class. The lace on it alone dazzles the eye!"

And so they began to entreat the peasant to take them to Redtape Avenue. And then they found, curiously enough, that the peasant himself had been there.

"Why, we are the generals from Redtape Avenue, you know!" exclaimed the generals in joyful chorus.

"And I, I am the man who paints the outside of a house, suspended from a rope, and walks on the roof like a fly. You may have noticed me sometimes." And he began to dance to amuse the generals. For had they not treated him kindly, this lazy vagabond, and condescended to accept his low-born service? So he built a boat in which they might sail over the sea to Redtape Avenue.

"But see to it that you don't drown us!" cried the generals, when they saw the frail craft rocking on the waves.

"Be easy, generals; I know what I am about," replied the peasant, and began his preparations for departure.

The peasant gathered up the feathers of swans, and with them covered the bottom of the boat, placed the generals in the center, made the sign of the cross over them, and set out. All manner of storms and high winds crossed their path, and the terror experienced by the generals can never be described; but the peasant never stopped rowing, except when he caught herrings with which to feed the travelers.

But at last they reached the Neva, and the great Katherine Canal, and the glorious Redtape Avenue. The cooks held up their hands in astonishment when they beheld their generals so fat and white and jolly! The generals drank their coffee, ate rolls with real butter, and donned their uniforms. Then they went to the Imperial Treasury, and pen cannot write, nor can tongue tell, what an enormous sum of money they each received there.

But they did not forget the poor peasant—not they. They gave him a glass of brandy and a silver five-copeck piece, with the salutation, "Your health, you great, stupid peasant!"

Anton Chekov

Genius

THE artist, Yegor Savich, who in the summer months boards with the widow of an officer, is sitting on the bed in his room in a state of extreme melancholy. Without, heavy rain-clouds are passing over the sky, and a cold, damp wind is drifting through the trees with plaintive sobbing. The air is full of yellow, faded leaves. Good-by, summer! This sadness of Nature is, in its way, beautiful and poetic, but Yegor Savich is not now in the mood for beauty. He is frightfully bored, and his only comfort lies in the thought that to-morrow he will have left the place. Bed, chairs, table, floor—all are covered with piles of pillows, rugs, and boxes. The curtains and blinds have been taken from the windows, and everything is in a state of disorder; for to-morrow they move back to town.

The lady of the house is not at home; she has gone somewhere to arrange for the moving. Her daughter Katya, a girl of twenty, is taking advantage of the absence of her strict mama by sitting the whole time in the young man's room. The artist is going to leave to-morrow, and she has still much to say to him. She talks and talks, yet she feels that she has not yet said the tenth part of what she must say. Sorrowfully and tenderly, her eyes filled with tears, she gazes at his untidy head. And untidy Yegor certainly is—fearfully and brutally untidy. His hair hangs down to his shoulders, his beard sprouts from his ears and nose, and even over his collar. His eyes are almost hidden

87

under his thick, overhanging brows—all the hair so dense and luxuriant that if a fly ever lost his way in it he would not find his way out before the Day of Judgment.

Yegor Savich listens to Katya's words, and yawns. When Katya bursts into tears, he looks at her suspiciously from under his hanging brows, frowns until his forehead becomes a mass of long wrinkles, and speaks in a heavy, funereal bass:

"I cannot marry you."

"Why?" asks Katya timidly.

"Because no painter, and especially no man who lives for art, should marry. An artist must be free."

"I would not hinder you in any way, Yegor Savich."

"I am speaking not of myself alone, but in general. Great writers and artists never marry."

"And you will be a great man, I understand that perfectly. But put yourself in my place for a moment. I am so afraid of mama. She is so strict, and has such a bad temper. If she knew that you were not going to marry me, she would certainly kill me at once. Oh, think of it! And then, you haven't paid your rent yet!"

"To the devil with it! I'll pay it some time."

Yegor Savich gets up and begins to walk up and down the room.

"I must go abroad," says he. And then the artist explains how easy it would be for him to travel abroad. All he had to do was to paint a picture and sell it.

"Of course!" agrees Katya. "But why didn't you paint one this summer?"

"Do you think a man can paint in this hovel?" breaks out the artist angrily. "And where do you think I could have found a model?"

Anton Chekov

Somewhere on the floor below a door slams. Katya, who had been momentarily expecting the return of her mother, jumps up from her chair and runs away. The artist remains alone. For a long time he paces the floor, picking his way through the mass of heaped-up articles. He can hear the widow moving crockery and reviling the porters, who have asked two rubles for the job. Full of bitterness, Yegor Savich stops before the sideboard and gazes reflectively at the brandy-bottle.

"If only some one did kill you," he hears the widow yell, as she falls upon the unlucky Katya, "it would be no great loss!"

The artist drinks a glass of brandy, and the black clouds that have been hovering over his soul brighten as though the sun has commenced to shine through them, and he feels as though his internal organs were laughing in chorus. He falls into a reverie. In fancy he sees his progress to greatness. His mind cannot quite clearly make out the subjects of his future pictures, but he sees distinctly what the newspapers say about him; his photographs are for sale in the shop-windows, and his colleagues are enviously looking round after him in the street. He strains his imagination violently to see himself sitting in some elegant drawing-room, surrounded by beautiful admirers; but this part of his dream takes a rather vague and uncertain shape, for never in his life has he seen a drawing-room, nor do the beautiful admirers stand out with the distinctness that he would like, for since the day of his birth he has never known a beautiful admirer, nor even a passably good-looking young woman. People who do not know life from personal experience usually picture it to themselves from books, but Yegor Savich had read no books. It is true that he had once started to read one by Gogol, but he had fallen asleep at the second page.

"If it won't burn, I'll make it burn!" snarls the widow somewhere below, engaged in heating the teakettle. "Katya, bring some more coal!"

The castle-building artist feels the necessity of communicating to some one else his hopes and dreams. He goes down-stairs to the kitchen, where the fat widow and Katya are so busy. There he seats himself on a bench near the kettle, and begins to talk:

"What a fine thing it is to be an artist! Wherever I want to go, there I go! What I wish to do, that I do. I need fill no office, plow no field. I have no duties and no master. I am my own master. Above all, my work is for the improvement of the human race!"

After the midday meal he throws himself upon his bed. He usually sleeps until evening, but to-day he is interrupted. Early in the afternoon he feels some one pulling at his leg. He opens his eyes and sees his friend Uklekin, the landscape-painter, who has spent the whole summer in the Kostroma province.

"Ah!" he joyfully shouts, "whom do I see?"

And now begins a torrent of hand-shakings and questions.

"Well, what have you brought with you? You must have a trunkful of sketches," says Yegor Savich, and looks on while Uklekin unpacks his bag.

"Oh, I have a few things with me. And you—have you painted anything?"

Yegor Savich stoops down behind the bed, and, red in the face, brings out a linen frame covered with dust and cobwebs.

Anton Chekov

" Here—a girl at the window after the farewell from her
lover," he says. " In three sittings—not nearly finished."

The picture represents Katya, who, however, is hardly even
drawn in outline, sitting at an open window; through the
window are to be seen a rail fence and a violet background.
Uklekin does not like the picture.

" Hm—there is a good deal of light and—and expression,"
he says. " You have the illusion of distance pretty well, but
that fence literally cries to Heaven—it shrieks!"

The brandy-bottle appears upon the scene.

Toward evening Yegor Savich is visited by his colleague
and neighbor, the historical painter Kostylov, a small man
of about thirty-three, who likewise is a beginner with splendid hopes. He has long hair, a blouse and collar like Shakespeare, and his motions are studied and impressive. When
he sees the bottle of brandy he knits his brows, and complains about the weakness of his chest, but is finally seduced
by the persuasions of his friends, and drinks a glass or two.

" I have a fine idea for a picture, my friends," he says,
after he has drunk himself into a slightly intoxicated state.
" I am going to paint a Nero, or a Herod, or some other
tyrant of the kind, you understand, and contrast him with
the idea of Christianity—on one side Rome, on the other,
you understand, Christianity. I will paint the spirit of it,
you understand—the spirit!"

And below, the widow cries, quite appropriately, " Katya,
bring the bottle here! You blockhead, go to Sidorov's and
get some beer!"

The colleagues, all three of them, stamp about from one
end of the room to the other, like wild beasts in a cage.
They talk unceasingly, enthusiastically, in chorus; all three
are excited, inspired. To hear them, you would imagine

that they held wealth, fame, and the future in their hands.
And it occurs to none of them that time is flying; that day
by day life is ebbing away; that they have long been eating
the bread of strangers, and as yet have done nothing; that
all three of them are victims of that relentless law which
says that out of the hundred who begin, only two or three
may succeed, and all the rest will go to earth. They are
content and happy, and look the future boldly in the face.

At two o'clock in the morning Kostylov takes his leave,
straightens his Shakespeare collar, and goes home. The
landscape-artist is to stay overnight with the other painter.
Before he goes to bed, Yegor Savich takes the lamp and
goes into the kitchen for a drink of water. In the dark,
narrow hall Katya is sitting on a trunk, her hands resting
on her knees, staring into vacancy. Her pale, rather coarse
face is transfigured by a sweet smile, and her eyes are
shining.

"What! you here?" asks Yegor Savich. "What are you
mooning about?"

"I am thinking of the time when you will be famous,"
she replies, half whispering. "I can see clearly before me
how great a man you will soon be. I heard everything you
said in there. I am dreaming—dreaming."

Katya breaks into a happy laugh, then she gives a gentle
sob, and devoutly folds her hands on the shoulder of her
divinity.—"*Humorous Stories.*"

Proverbs

The worst brandy is better than water.

The path to the law court is wide; the path away from it is narrow.

Even when drowning, a man wants company.

Cherish your wife as you would your salvation, and beat her as you would your coat.

A bad peace is superior to a good quarrel.

Spare the peasant your lash, but not his rubles.

Poverty is not a sin, but it's a great deal worse.

In a storm, pray to the Lord and keep on rowing as hard as you can.

A sparrow is small; still, it's a bird.

If your wife were a guitar, you could hang her up after playing.

An old crow never croaks without reason.

A dozen axes may be left together; two spindles must be kept apart.

A dog is wiser than a woman, for it does not turn upon its master.

To the badness in his wares the seller is blind.

Good luck departs—like your hair; bad luck remains—like your nails.

Ignatji Potapenko

The Course in Sanskrit

I CAME to Paris without any definite purpose. I had been teaching for twelve years, and recreation was all I sought for. I counted on my small inheritance to keep me for six years; then I could go home again and work. Well, when one gets to Paris, of course one must visit something. So I visited the theaters, at times the big shops, often the museums, always with the feeling that it was all rather unsatisfactory. And so I determined to study a bit, and to hear lectures at the Sorbonne University. I went to one professor, to a second, to a third. The lectures interested me, and I attend some of them yet. But one day the rather strange idea came to me of hearing some lectures on the Sanskrit language. Like all moderately well-educated people, I knew that it was a very old language, that philologists were fond of talking about it, that it seemed never to have been spoken, but recorded in books alone, and that all European languages sustained a certain relation to it. Perhaps my sudden interest was foolish. No matter, I went.

When I arrived at the lecture-hall I stopped at the threshold. Could I have mistaken the number? Not at all. The benches for the auditors stood there in the usual solemn rows, only there was not a single student to be seen. So I concluded that I had come too soon, and was about to leave, when suddenly from behind an enormous blackboard a curious little figure appeared. It was a little, wizened, dried-up man clad in a dress suit with enormous tails. His head was

94

bald and polished, and his face puckered with innumerable wrinkles.

"Ah, madam!" he exclaimed joyfully, and approached me with outstretched hands, "were you really intending to go away again? Perhaps you thought I was not here; but I am here—to be sure I am. Will you be pleased to take a seat? So; now we can begin our lecture."

I confess that I was dumfounded. I sat down with so astonished an expression that the old gentleman made haste to explain the condition of things to me.

"It is a very good thing that you wish to take my course. Few care to take it—very few, as you perceive. My subject is not for the many, and I am not sorry for that. Indeed, I have but one regular student, and he lives in Saint Cloud, so that he can come only twice a month, whereas I must lecture every week. Well—let us begin. I am confident that I can show you how interesting my subject really is."

He went up to his platform, sat down next to his desk, and began:

"Madam, we are naturally very far advanced in our studies, seeing that the course began in October. But, in consideration of the fact that you are here for the first time, I shall try to give you in a few words an insight into the elements of our subject. The Sanskrit tongue——"

And so on, and so on. The old gentleman lectured with enthusiasm, and pitched his voice as loud as though he were oblivious of the emptiness of the lecture-hall. He wished to be heard by the last bench as well as by the first. In short, it was a *bona-fide* lecture, and it certainly was a peculiar sensation to have a professor of the Sorbonne lecture for one's sole benefit.

When he had finished, he put off the professor, and became

a French gentleman anxious to be courteous to a lady. He smiled, and showed a row of well-preserved teeth. "And now," said he, "you will permit me to introduce myself to you—Professor X. I am very, very glad that you propose to study under me; and, as time goes on, you will understand everything very clearly, and realize how fascinating our subject is. And now, may I ask for your name?"

"Mlle. Rostchin."

"Ah, you are a Russian. Delighted! I do not care much for politics. Still, we are friends. Then, too, Russian ladies are, as a rule, most zealous and intelligent students. You will become an admirable Sanskrit scholar; and it will give me a special pleasure to supply you with the necessary books. Will you permit me to do so? Here"—he took an elegant card-case from his pocket and handed me a card—"here is my address. I shall be charmed if you will call on me. Yes, I am married, father of a family—have, in fact, grown daughters. Otherwise I would not venture— Ah, good-by for the present!"

What was I to do? I could not well refuse. The old gentleman had been so kind and courteous to me; it pleased him so profoundly to have a student. With his difficult and esoteric subject he had probably never succeeded in having more than half a dozen hearers. The other student at present —the gentleman who lived at Saint Cloud—came only twice a month. And so I was quite an event in the old gentleman's life. How would he feel if I were absent from the next lecture—if the real flesh-and-blood lady who was interested in Sanskrit faded again into the void? How empty and lonely the place would be! How would he meet his wife and daughters, to whom he has been full of talk concerning his new student?

Ignatji Potapenko

In short, I was sorry for the old gentleman. I had it not in me to overthrow his hopes. Therefore, three days later I went to call on him.

He lived in a modest little apartment on the fifth floor of a house in the narrow Rue de Colombe. I was most pleasantly received. The professor's wife was a charming Alsatian; his two daughters genuine French girls, who assured me in all seriousness that only Russia, with its extremely cold climate, could produce ladies who were interested in Sanskrit. Quite contrary to French custom, oranges were served, with other fruits, biscuits, and cordials.

And then my old gentleman gave me a pile of books and pamphlets concerning Sanskrit, and again expressed his opinion that I would become an admirable scholar in his subject.

I went away laden with books, so that I had to take a cab at once. Thus I was committed to the study of Sanskrit. And I studied it honestly, and my intelligent questions and progress made the old gentleman's life bright. I had not the heart to miss a single lecture.

At last I met my fellow student from Saint Cloud. He was a man well advanced in years, and used a crutch. I asked him if he was very much interested in Sanskrit. He answered me with great seriousness.

"You see," he said, "I live out in Saint Cloud, where I manufacture certain chemicals on a small scale. Twice a month I get to Paris to buy new material and sell my product. Now, my business makes it necessary for me to wait each time from one to three o'clock. I am a simple, sober man; I care neither for the *cafés,* nor for the noise and hurry of the Paris streets; so I wait here, where it is cool, quiet, instructive—and costs nothing!"—*"Tales and Sketches."*

Maxim Pyeshkov—"Gorki"

Promtov's Marriage

At last I married. A man of my disposition only does a
thing like that either from being bored or while he is drunk.
My wife was a clergyman's daughter, and lived with her
mother, the father having died. When I married her she
owned a nice little house—or, rather, a pretty large house—
and a fair sum of money. She was a good-looking, intelligent, cheerful sort of young woman, but she had a great
passion for reading books, which had a bad effect on both
of us. She was always fishing some wise maxim or other out
of her blessed books, and whenever she had caught one she
would come to me with it. But I never could endure moral
reflections, not even as a child. At first I laughed at my
wife, but she was incorrigible, and I could listen to her
solemn speeches no longer. I always think of her as spouting some pompous phrase out of a book. Book-learning suits
a woman about as well as a dress coat looks on a bootblack.
Well, of course we took to quarreling.

About that time I made the acquaintance of a minor canon
of the Orthodox Church—a merry soul, though a bit loose
in his habits. He could strum on the guitar and sing songs;
no one could beat him at dancing a breakdown, nor at drinking brandy either. I liked him better than anybody in the
whole town, because he brought life into that dismal house
of ours. My wife did nothing but scold me for my friend-
ship with the minor canon, and did her utmost to draw me

into her gang of literary people and humbugs. Every evening she received the visits of "the most serious and respectable people of the town," as she put it. She was right: they looked as serious as if they had been hanged.

I was rather fond of reading myself in those days, only nothing I ever read bothered me in the least, and I don't see why it should have. But those people—I mean my wife and her worthy friends—got so terribly excited from reading a book that one might have imagined their hair was being pulled out. My idea is this: a book—well, what of it? A book's a book; if it's a good one, so much the better. But, after all, a book is only written by an individual, and he no wiser than the rest of us. All books are written for the same purpose. They all try to prove that what's good is good, and what's bad is bad. Read a hundred volumes, or a thousand, none of them can alter a single fact. But my wife gobbled down print by the ton, so that I finally told her I should have done better to marry the minor canon instead of her. He was the only person who saved me from being bored to death. If it had not been for him, I should simply have decamped, and left my wife to kick her heels alone. As soon as her Philistines appeared I would rush off to see the minor canon.

In this way a year and a half went by. Merely for the sake of something to do I frequently helped the minor canon with the service. Sometimes I would read out the Gospel, and sometimes I would stand up before the organ and chant the words of the Psalmist, "Many a time have they afflicted me from my youth." I really had to endure a great deal, and at the Judgment Day I shall probably be excused a good many of my sins by way of reward.

One day a niece of the minor canon arrived. He had sent

for her, in the first place, because he wanted company, and then because he had been eaten by pigs—not entirely, but still enough to damage his beauty very much. The poor fellow had fallen down in the yard, after drinking too much, and gone sound asleep. While he lay there, just like a log, out came the pigs from their sty and gnawed away at his ears and cheeks and neck. Pigs enjoy any sort of garbage. Well, that did for the minor canon, and he was laid up. So he sent for his niece. She was to nurse him, and I was to entertain her. We went at our duties with heart and soul, and succeeded remarkably well. But, of course, my wife got wind of the story, and flew into a temper. She abused me fearfully, and, not knowing what to answer, what could I do but return the abuse? Then she told me to get out of her house. Well, I thought the matter over, and finally decided to leave her house—and the town, too, while I was about it.

That was the end of my marriage. If she is still alive—my wife, I mean—I suppose she considers me as dead. I have never had the least inclination to see her again. I dare say she has completely forgotten me by this time, and is quite happy. But, heavens, how she bored me!

—*"Autobiography of a Vagabond."*

Surgical Operation Upon a Human Heart

It was Twelfth Night, and Ivan Ivanovich Ivanov was sitting alone in his study. Judged by his mental qualities, he was an "intellectual person"; his aim, however, was to reach moral perfection, which he tried to acquire through discussions with friends and the reading of instructive books. He was meditating, on this eve of a solemn religious festival, over his doings of the past fortnight, and was so deeply absorbed in this pursuit that he failed to notice how a snowflake got into the room and changed into a small imp. A man examining himself resembles Narcissus and a fly stuck in a jar of honey as well.

With his eyes closed, Ivan Ivanovich tried to recall to his mind a picture he had recently seen in an illustrated periodical. It represented a huge octopus. "That," reflected our pensive friend, "bears exactly on my own case. All my life I have been the victim of an octopus sucking out the essence of my soul. I do my utmost to free myself from the monster, to overcome my evil passions; but again and again I am seized by those dreadful tentacles, and drawn into vile debauches, where a man forgets every decent instinct and turns into a beast. I ought really to exert all my will and all my brain to develop into a perfect man. I ought to make a bold fight for my individuality. Yes, I really ought to. But, instead, what have I been doing this last fortnight? Three masked balls—a woman—beautiful, Lord! how beautiful! But still she is somebody else's wife—a woman on whom I have no claim. Well, let me see, though. Hm— yes, I have a sort of claim. After all, Yegor being an old friend of mine, quite an intimate friend, and she being married to him—now that ought to make some difference. It ought to make my—ah—error not quite so—not quite so— pronounced. At any rate, it's a good thing I always acknowledge my own faults; it gives me a better opinion of myself— raises me in my own estimation, as it were—which is highly gratifying. But, the devil take it! why can't I tear those unruly passions out of my heart?"

"You might try," he heard a voice observe, in a polite, pleasant tone. "If you would allow me, I might perhaps assist you."

Ivan Ivanovich looked up, and quaked. One always quakes at the sight of a demon.

"I beg your pardon," he addressed the visitor; "I was not aware you had come in. If I am not mistaken, I have the honor of speaking to——"

"Yes, precisely; and I beg you will not let me disturb you," interposed the imp.

"Ah, indeed! and—hm—what may it be that procures me the pleasure of your visit?"

"I merely happened to be passing by. This is Twelfth Night, you know, when all we poor devils are kicked out from everywhere. It's foggy and damp out-of-doors; in fact, we are having a bad winter this year; and you being known to me as a humane person——"

Ivan Ivanovich was embarrassed. He had never taken the existence of infernal spirits very seriously.

"I—I'm—ah—delighted!" said he, with a faint smile. "Perhaps you are not quite comfortably seated on the window-sill. Permit me to——"

"Oh, pray don't apologize! Like yourself, I am used to adapting myself to any sort of situation, however undesirable it may be."

"Very obliging, I'm sure," said Ivan Ivanovich, while observing to himself how amiable the visitor was.

"You were expressing a wish, were you not, to change your heart in some way?"

"I was. You see, in spite of the great march of the human intellect, one occasionally finds oneself rather weak when assailed by one's passions. But excuse me: if I understood you rightly, you—ah—offered me your assistance in this—this particular enterprise."

"I certainly did, and repeat that it will be a privilege to afford you my help."

"But would that not be contrary to your—hm—nature?"

"Dear me, Ivan Ivanovich!" exclaimed the devil, as he let his arms dangle to and fro, "do you think I am not tired of my nature?"

"Perhaps so."

"Of course it's so! A man, too, in time gets tired of doing nothing but evil, and sometimes even repents."

"What if I accepted his offer?" soliloquized the other. "He has the power to do anything, and could make me morally perfect. How astonished my friends would be!"

"Well, you seem to have scruples," remarked the demon.

"Hm—you see, I fancy the operation must be extremely painful."

"Only to those who have stern hearts, those who are inflexible."

"And what about me?"

"You—pardon me, I speak as a physician might—you have a pulpy, flaccid sort of heart, something like an over-ripe radish. If I were to remove the passions which incommode you from your heart, you would feel like a hen having feathers pulled out of her tail."

Ivan Ivanovich pondered the matter for some time, and then resumed:

"Allow me a question: In return for this service, do you ask for my soul?"

The devil jumped down from the window-sill, began scraping the floor violently with his hoofs, and ejaculated:

"Your soul? Oh, no—not at all, I assure you! Why, what should I do with your soul, my dear sir? I mean— I beg your pardon—what use would it be to me? No, really, I assure you!"

Ivan Ivanovich observed that the devil was quite excited and annoyed.

"I only asked because I thought it was the custom."

"So it was, a long time ago, when we could get healthy, strong souls."

"Am I to infer that you have a poor opinion of mine?"

"Oh, certainly not! But I am asking for no remuneration at present. And then, of course, you will acknowledge my interest in a perfect individual."

"Indeed? And—and you say the operation would be neither painful—nor—nor—dangerous?"

"Be easy on that point, my dear sir. You will have absolutely nothing to sacrifice through reaching perfection by my assistance. If you agree, I might take something out of your heart just by way of trial."

"Ye—y-e-s."

"That's capital, now! Tell me, what feeling is it that troubles you most?"

The patient of the infernal physician reflected. It is difficult to decide which of one's passions one would be most willing to expel. At last he replied:

"Let us begin with the least conspicuous."

"All the same to me. What is your disorder, then?"

Another silence. Although Ivan Ivanovich was an adept at self-inspection, or because that very process tended to internal chaos, he could make nothing out of the actual state of his heart. It was all muddle and confusion. However much he probed, he could not find a single positive, direct emotion with an independent, uncolored existence. Meanwhile the proposition came from the other side:

"Supposing we remove ambition from your heart. You have little of that, I believe?"

"Very well," came the reluctant answer; "pull it out."

The imp approached him and touched his breast with his hand, which he withdrew sharply. Ivan Ivanovich experienced a vivid yet not unpleasant twinge, analogous to that accompanying the extraction of a splinter from one's finger.

"Why, that scarcely hurt at all!" he exclaimed, in a tone of relief. "Will you please let me look at my ambition?"

The devil held out his hand. On it lay a minute, crumpled-up object, in color and texture very much like a rag long in use for wiping dust off furniture. Its former possessor gazed at it, and sighed. "When I remember," said he, "that it is really a piece of my heart, I feel sorry for it."

"Would you not like me to pull out your compassion?"

"But how am I to do without it?"

"What use is it to you?"

"Well, it—it gives one a comforting—ah—pleasant sort of sensation, you know."

"What about malice, then?"

"Oh! out with it, by all means! To the devil with it! I beg your pardon—I didn't mean—I——"

"No, not at all—don't apologize." And the minister of darkness once more touched the breast of the mortal, who again felt the same kind of twinge. And, as before, the devil held something resembling a rag in his hand. Only it diffused a rancid smell.

"So that is what my malice looks like?"

"There is a considerable mixture of cowardice in it."

"You don't say so! But tell me, why are my emotions so flabby?"

"Made that way," replied the fiend, as he contemptuously flung a bit of the heart into a corner.

"I am beginning to feel quite peculiar," the patient went on.

"Better?"

"I feel lighter, easier, about the chest."

"Shall we continue with the operation?"

"Yes, certainly."

"What else is the matter with you?"

"Oh, all sorts of things! All the usual things."

"Anger, for instance?"

"Of course—yes. Anger—well—I mean—it's not only that, but there is also nervousness, irritability, an uncertain state of temper."

"Shall I take it out?"

"If you please. But I must beg you to be careful. You see, things are rather mixed up inside me. Now, while you were taking out my malice, I experienced a sensation like shame."

"Natural enough," was the satanic comment. "Even I blush for you at the sight of your feelings. You keep your heart in very bad condition."

"Is it my fault?" asked Ivan Ivanovich. "A heart is not a set of teeth. You cannot keep it clean with brush and powder."

"True, true. But do you wish me to go on? Shall I free you from your nervousness?"

"Yes, that would suit me very well."

When the messenger from below held out his palm for the third time, there lay on it a small spongy lump of indefinite composition. It had no particular shape, sent forth an odor of putridity, and was of double hue: one color was a grayish green, like unripe fruit, the other a greenish brown, like decaying fruit. The demon inspected the quivering, gall-like substance with much curiosity, endeavoring to determine its character. "Now," said he, "I have taken something out of you, and have no idea what it is. Such treasures as you have garnered up in your heart during your thirty years of life! This specimen would be too much for a chemist. But I assume that now, being relieved of all that muck, you are as pure as an angel. What a prime surgeon I am! I never suspected myself of such proficiency. I congratulate you, my friend, on your clean heart, and on your moral perfection, or whatever you call it. I hope that you have now reached the perfection of perfectibility." Upon which the devil threw away what he had in his hand.

But Ivan Ivanovich had utterly collapsed. There he sat, weak, limp, doubled up, as though there was not a single bone in his body, his mouth agape, and an expression of unspeakable bliss fixed on his face, such as may frequently be observed on the countenances of born idiots.

"Don't you hear me?" asked the imp.

"Ah——"

"What is the matter with you?"

"Oh——"

"Do you feel anything queer?"

"Uh——"

"Are you ill?"

"Eh——"

"Why," exclaimed the evil spirit, "this is like magic! I wonder if I have actually pulled his whole substance out of him?—Listen to me, I say!"

"Ah——"

" Astonishing! Nothing left but a few feeble sounds without any meaning! What shall I do with him?" And he tapped Ivan Ivanovich on the chest, the result being a dull rumble, as of an empty barrel.

" So this is a perfect man! Well, well—poor creature! Quite void—quite hollow! I had no idea he was so full of badness. But the question is, What can be done with him now?"

The devil became absorbed in thought, while continuing to gaze upon the settled smile of transfiguration proper to one whose aim was reached.

" Aha!" suddenly ejaculated the imp, " I know! A fine inspiration! And it will please my friends too. First, I'll hang up this specimen of perfection to dry, and then I'll shake some peas into it. That will make a nice rattle for the small fry at home to play with."

Whereupon the devil lifted Ivan Ivanovich from the chair, folded him up, clapped him under his arm, and vanished into the night.—" *Adventures of a Devil.*"

Danish Wit and Humor

Ludvig von Holberg

The Human Planet and the Griffin

MY downward course having now continued for some time, I began to observe that the rapidity with which I was first precipitated gradually abated as I approached the planet, or celestial globe, which I had perceived soon after the beginning of my descent. As I drew nearer, it appeared visibly to increase in bulk, so that at length I could discern, although through a cloudy atmosphere that surrounded it, seas, hills, and valleys upon the surface.

I now became fully sensible that I was not only suspended and dangling in the celestial air, but that the perpendicular line, in which I had hitherto descended, was now changed into a circle. At this discovery I must acknowledge my hair stood on end, fearing, as I did, that I must be metamorphosed either into a planet or a satellite, to be twirled round in perpetual motion to the world's end. When I, however, considered within myself that my reputation and honor were in no wise likely to be tarnished through such a circumstance, and that a celestial globe, or at least the satellite of a celestial globe, always proceeding in planetary order, was at any time able to outshine and eclipse a poor, hungry student of philosophy, my spirits again revived; and the more so when I found that the celestial air in which I hung had so strongly fortified me against the cravings of nature that I felt neither hunger nor thirst. I just then remembered that I had a biscuit in my pocket. I took it out, merely to try, out of curiosity, whether in that condition I could relish it; but, on taking the first mouthful, I quickly perceived that all earthly food had become nauseous; I therefore cast it away from me as a useless encumbrance. How great was my amazement on this occasion, when I discovered that the biscuit not only hung dangling in the air, but—wonderful to relate!—began to describe a planetary orbit around me. This gave me a clear perception of the true laws of motion, according to which all bodies placed in equipoise must move in circles.

However much I might have felt dejected but a short time previous, at seeing myself a ball in the hands of mocking Fate, I was now, on the other hand, equally elated on beholding myself exalted not only to a self-subsisting planet, but to such an one even as would always be attended by a moon, and therefore ought to be ranked among stars of the first magnitude, or planets of the first order. In acknowledging the whole of my vain imbecility, I must needs say that I was so immoderately inflated by this good fortune, that had I then met with all the burgomasters and all the senators of Bergen, I would merely have vouchsafed them a single glance, in order to have looked down upon them as insignificant atoms; nor would I have deigned to incline my eyes, much less to bow my head, to them.

In this state I remained three whole days. As I was continually carried round by and with the planet, which was now at no very great distance from me, I could easily distinguish the day from the night, through observing the rising and the setting of the subterranean sun; though after he was gone down I never remarked any such nights as we experience on earth. For when this bright luminary went even far below the horizon, the heavens everywhere still continued light and shining, very similar to the full moon with us. This brightness, I concluded, must be reflected from the internal

Ludvig von Holberg

vault of the hemisphere of this world, which borrowed its light from a sun placed in the center. A superficial knowledge of astronomy assisted me in drawing this inference.

But the most ridiculous part of my conduct, while enjoying my happy state, was, perhaps, that I looked upon myself as coming next after the immortal gods; and, as I considered myself in the quality of a new celestial light, I made account of being speedily introduced, together with my satellite, into the catalogue of stars, by the astronomers of the globe below; when, lo! there appeared a most hideous and terrific winged monster, which first threatened my right side, and then my left, now my front, and afterward my rear, with a deadly attack. In the beginning, as it approached me, I took it to be one of the twelve signs of the zodiac, and secretly wished in my heart, if that really were the case, that it might be the Virgin; for, out of the whole stellar system, no one save her could, in that solitude, show me the smallest particle of motherly care or afford me the least consolation. As this creature, however, drew nearer to me, I perceived that it was neither more nor less than a frightful griffin. I was, in consequence of this discovery, so stupefied and so overtaken with fear, that I nearly forgot myself and my new celestial dignity, and, in my inexpressible anxiety and perplexity of mind, I drew out the testimonials I had received from the university, which, as good luck would have it to be, were then in my pocket, to exhibit to this dreadful menacing enemy, and to prove that I had passed both my theological and philosophical examinations, was a scholar, and, what was more, possessor of the baccalaureate. As soon, however, as the first heat of my passion was over, I gradually recovered my reason, and laughed heartily at the folly of which I was guilty.

Danish Wit and Humor

I could still not clearly perceive for what purpose the griffin followed me. I knew not whether to look upon him as an enemy or as a friend, or to believe—which was probable—that merely from curiosity he was indulging in a little contemplation of my form. True it is that a human body suspended in the air, with a boat-hook in his hand, and dragging a long rope after him, would be a sufficiently ludicrous sight to attract any one to stop and gaze after it. The extraordinary figure that I then cut, occasioned, as I afterward learned, the inhabitants on my side of the planet to hold diverse controversial colloquies, and to form several hypotheses concerning me. The philosophers and astronomers took me to be a comet, and judged the rope to be the comet's tail. Many even insisted that so uncommon an appearance in the heavens must portend some unusual calamity, not short of pestilence or famine. Others, again, went much farther—even far beyond the possibility of observation—and with much precision delineated my form; so that, before my arrival on the globe, I was already defined, described, painted, and even engraved on copper.

All this I afterward heard mentioned with inward merriment, and a sort of tickling delight, when I had been for some time upon the planet, and had learned the subterranean language.

But to resume. The griffin had now approached near enough to attack me with his wings, and was even on the point of assaulting me with his foot; so that I could plainly discern with what view he paid me his visit. I therefore commenced a defensive attack against this formidable and warlike enemy; took the boat-hook in both hands, and not only with it parried off his audacious attacks, but sometimes even forced him to retreat in haste; until at length, after many a fruitless blow, while he still continued to tug at me, I succeeded in passing the hook between his wings, and sticking it into the nape of his neck with such force that I was unable to draw it out again. The wounded monster, with a horrid shriek, now flew headlong to the planet beneath; and I, weary already of my new celestial astro-dignity, was glad to change my orbital motion to its former perpendicularity.

—" *Niels Klim's Underground Journey.*"

Judicial Decisions

ABRAHAMS *and* SANDERUS.

Ab. I'll tell you of a little trick that will make the whole town laugh. Do you know what plan I've made with three or four of our most prominent men?

San. I know nothing about it.

Ab. Do you know Herman of Bremen?

San. Yes; if I'm not mistaken, that's the great pewterer-politician who lives in the house over there.

Ab. That's the man. The other day I was in the company of several counselors who were very angry at the man because he criticizes the government very freely in all the taverns, and talks about reforming everything. The counselors were deciding to send some people to report on his speeches, and to punish him as a warning example.

San. It is indeed right that fellows of that kind should be severely dealt with. They sit over their beer and hold forth against kings, counselors, and all constituted authorities. They are dangerous, too, for the common people fail to see the humor of it if some pewterer, hat or brush maker talks about such things without the least knowledge of them.

Ab. Quite true. Such a pewterer-politician will smelt the whole Roman empire for you in the time it takes him to make one plate. And yet I don't like the plan of the counselors. For to punish such a man or to throw him into prison excites the mob and gives prestige to a fool. I would prefer to play a comedy at his expense. The result would be better.

San. And what do you propose to do?

Ab. We can send him a pretended deputation from the town, congratulating him upon his election to the mayoralty, and then give him, in virtue of his office, some very difficult cases to decide. It will soon be seen how badly he manages, and what a difference there is between talking about a thing and really understanding it.

San. And what will the result be?

Ab. Either that he will simply turn tail, or, confessing his inability, ask to be released from the office. I have therefore come to ask for your assistance in the matter, as I know how inventive you are.

San. Yes, we might manage it. We could impersonate a deputation ourselves.

.   .   .   .   .   .

HERMAN OF BREMEN; HENRIK, *his Apprentice; two* LAWYERS.

1st Law. From the very depths of our hearts we wish your Mayorship blessings and honor in the new dignity that has come to you in this city, and we trust that you will be behind none of your predecessors in clemency, wisdom, and *bon ton.* The more so as your Magnificence has reached this exalted station not through wealth, friends, or influence, but

Ludvig von Holberg

through your well-known virtues, and your learning and experience in matters of statesmanship.

Her. Très humble serviteur!

2d Law. And thus we rejoice to acknowledge an authority over us who is not only gifted with the highest wisdom——

Her. Yes, thank God for that!

2d Law. But who is also, as is well known, graciously inclined to hear the complaints of all who are burdened, and to have justice done them. Hence, in coming here to-day to offer you our most devoted felicitations, we take the opportunity of presenting for the judgment of your Magnificence a dispute that has arisen between our clients. Both parties had, indeed, determined to have the case tried according to the law of the land, but after mature deliberation, and in order to save the loss of time and money inseparable from a public trial, we decided to leave the case to the decision of your Mayorship.

(HERMAN *sits down. The others remain standing.*)

1st Law. Our clients are neighbors, whose properties are divided by a brook. Now it happened, about three years ago, that the water washed a tract of land from the property of my client and added it to that of his opponent. Now, may the latter keep it? Does not the law say: *Nemo ulterius damno debet locupletari?* But my opponent's client wants to enrich himself at the expense of mine. That in itself is an offense *contra æquitatem naturalem.* Is it not so, your Mayorship?

Her. Yes; the proceeding does seem unreasonable. You are right, sir.

2d Law. But Justinian says very clearly, *Libro secundo institutionum titulo primo de alluvione——*

Her. Who the devil cares for what Justinian or Alexander the Great may have said! Both lived several thousands of years ago, probably before Hamburg was built. How can they judge of a case that did not occur in their day?

2d Law. I trust that your Mayorship will not attempt to set aside the laws that are recognized throughout Germany?

Her. Why—not exactly—no! You did not quite understand me. I merely meant to say—(*he coughs*)—be so good as to give me some further information in this matter.

2d Law. The exact words of Justinian are: *Quod per alluvionem agro tuo flumen adjecit jure gentium tibi adgiuritur.*

Her. My dear sir, you say that so rapidly; and, furthermore, your Latin pronunciation is very poor. If you use your mother tongue, we shall get on much better. I do not say this because I have no love for the Latin tongue. I sometimes sit for hours and talk Latin with my servant. Don't I, Henrik?

Hen. Yes, it's remarkable to hear you speak Latin. The tears start into my eyes when I think of it. The words run so rapidly from his mouth, they sound like peas boiling in a pot. Heaven only knows how any one can do it!

2d Law. Justinian's words are as follows, most honored Mayor: Whatever a river, by the action of its water, adds to your domain, that, by the law of nations, is yours.

Her. Yes, Justinian was quite right; he was an excellent person. I value his judgment too highly to dispute it.

1st Law. But, your Mayorship, my opponent quotes the law as the devil does Scripture. He leaves out the words that follow: *per alluvionem autem videtur id adjici, quod ita paulatim adjicitur, ut intelligi non possit, quantum quoque temporis momento adjiciatur.*

Her. Messieurs, your pardon. It's half past five, and I

must go to the town hall. Henrik, try to settle those people's affairs outside on the stairs.

1st Law. But will you not give us any opinion?

Her. You are both right—each in his way.

2d Law. But how can we be both in the right? If I am right, my opponent must be wrong. Justinian certainly is on my side.

Her. I am sorry, but I must go.

1st Law. (*holding* HERMAN *back*). You must grant me that I am right.

Her. It is true, Justinian seems to support both of you. Then why don't you come to an agreement? You don't know Justinian as well as I do. When he looks both ways, he means to say: Go, rascals, and come to a peaceable understanding!

2d Law. But, your Mayorship, in order to interpret the meaning of a lawgiver it is necessary to compare passages. Now, in the next paragraph he says: *Quod si vis fluminis de tuo prædio——*

Her. I wish you would leave me in peace! Don't you hear that I have to go?

1st Law. But just listen to what Hugo Grotius says.

Her. I don't care a straw either for you or your Hugo Grotius. Henrik, turn these fellows out!

(*Exeunt* HENRIK *with* LAWYERS. HENRIK *is heard in violent altercation outside. He is thrown into the room, followed by a* WOMAN *who seems to be a man in disguise. The* WOMAN *seizes* HERMAN *by the collar.*)

Woman. It is a fine mayor and fine laws that permit a man to have two wives! Don't you fear the vengeance of God?

Her. Woman, are you crazy? Who ever thought of such a thing?

Woman. I won't go till I see your blood!

Her. Help! Help! Henrik!

Enter HENRIK, *who pulls the* WOMAN *away, and pushes her out of the door.*

Her. Henrik, never you dare again to admit such women —or lawyers! They almost kill one. If other people come, tell them to be sure not to speak Latin to me, as, for a very particular reason, I have given up talking it.

Hen. I have given it up for the same reason.

Her. You may tell them I speak only Greek.

(*Some one knocks at the door.*)

Hen. (*goes out, and returns with a package of legal documents*). Here are some documents from the syndic, which you are requested to look through and give an opinion on.

Her. (*sits down and looks through the papers*). It is not as easy to be mayor as I thought it would be. Henrik, here are some things that I am supposed to look through, which the devil himself would not understand. (*He begins to write, gets up, wipes his forehead, and strikes out what he has written.*) Henrik!

Hen. Sir?

Her. Why are you so noisy? Can't you keep still?

Hen. I didn't move.

Her. (*takes off his wig, so as to think with more ease*). Henrik!

Hen. Sir?

Her. The devil take you! Stand still! You disturb me in my mental processes.

Ludvig von Holberg

Hen. Why, I did nothing but see whether my new livery was not too long.

Her. (*knocks his fist against his forehead*). Henrik!

Hen. Sir?

Her. Go out and tell the oyster-venders that their shouts disturb me in my political business.

Hen. (*opens the window and cries*). Hullo, you rascals! Do you dare to bellow in the mayor's street, and disturb him in his business?

Her. Henrik!

Hen. Sir?

Her. Stop, you ass!

Hen. It does no good, either. There are so many that as soon as you get rid of them, others begin; and——

Her. Not another word! Keep still, and don't move. (*Attempts to sit down again, but misses the chair, and falls on the floor.*) Henrik!

Hen. Sir?

Her. I'm lying on the ground!

Hen. I see you are.

Her. Why don't you come and help me?

Hen. Because you told me not to move.

Her. (*gets up again*). Isn't some one knocking?

Hen. Yes. (*At door.*) Whom do you wish to see?

1st Citizen. I am a hatter. I have a complaint to lay before the mayor.

Hen. Here is a hatter, with a complaint.

Her. Ask him to state the nature of his complaint.

Citizen. It is very complicated. I must see the mayor. Still, it will take no more than an hour, for my complaint contains only twenty points.

Her. May the Lord help me!

1st Citizen. Oh, your Mayorship, I have suffered great wrong, as your Honor will find when you hear my complaint.

Her. You must put it in writing.

Citizen. I have it here—four sheets.

Her. Henrik, some one else is knocking.

Hen. (*at door*). Whom do you wish to see?

2d Citizen. I want to complain against the hatter.

Hen. It's the other man's opponent.

Her. Let him give you his documents. Now, good people, remain outside, both of you. Henrik!

Hen. Yes, sir?

Her. Can't you help me to settle these things? I don't know how to begin. Read the hatter's complaint.

(HENRIK *reads.*)

Her. Enough, Henrik! I see that the man is right.

Hen. I always thought that a judge ought to hear both sides before coming to a conclusion. Shall I read the other's paper?

Her. Yes, read it.   (HENRIK *reads.*)

Hen. Well, both cannot be right.

Her. But who is right?

Hen. God and the mayor ought to know.

Her. The whole thing is utter confusion. Can't you help me to decide, stupid? What do I pay you your wages for?— What is that noise out there?

Hen. Those two are fighting.

Her. Go and tell them to have more respect for the mayor's house.

Hen. Isn't it better to let them fight it out? Why, great heavens! I believe they intend to force their way in! Listen to them thundering on the door.

(HERMAN *hides under the table.*)

120

Ludvig von Holberg

Hen. (*at door*). Who's there?

A Lackey. I have come from a foreign official. My master has some very important business to transact with the mayor.

Hen. (*looking about*). Where is the mayor? Did the devil fetch the mayor?

Her. (*whispers from under the table*). Who is it?

Hen. A foreign official wants to speak to you.

Her. Ask him to come back in half an hour. Tell him two hatters are here. Tell them to come to-morrow. Heaven help me! I'm at my wits' ends! Henrik, can't you advise something?

Hen. I think it would be best for his Mayorship to hang himself.

Her. Go into the next room and get me my political code. Perhaps I'll find some directions in it.

Hen. Shall I bring mustard and butter, too, for the cod?

Her. No; it isn't a fish—it's a book, bound in white leather. (*While* HENRIK *is away,* HERMAN *absent-mindedly tears up the hatter's document.*)

Hen. Here is the book. But what is that you are tearing up? Why, it's the hatter's complaint!

Her. Heavens! I had forgotten all about that! (*Takes book from* HENRIK, *and, after hastily looking over a few leaves, throws it on the floor.*) I think I had better take your advice, and hang myself!—"*The Pewterer-Politician.*"

Adam Oehlenschläger

Poison for a Fly

ALADDIN *and* APOTHECARY.

Alad. (*aside*).   Oh, bliss of blisses, to have found my love,
And 'scaped the clutches of impending death!
Yes, I shall hurl her tyrant from his throne.
The clear, bright springtime dances through my blood,
And all my boyhood's gamesomeness comes back.
See yonder silly druggist, how he stands
The picture of an overblown conceit!
Necessity commands me to employ
Fell poison's deadly chalice.   Be it so!
But since 'tis stern necessity commands,
Since virtue needs must come to grips with vice,
Banter and whim, as music does in war,
Shall drown the wail and anguish of the fray.
(*Aloud.*)   Good friend, I'd wager me a trifle now,
You are the owner of this shop yourself.
    Apoth.   And who may you be, pray, that crow so loud?
    Alad.   I've just arrived from Alexandria.
I clean the boots, or, to be more precise,
The slippers of a great philosopher.
    Apoth.   What want you?
    Alad.   Friend, canst read?
    Apoth.   Scarce were I else a pharmacopolist.
    Alad.   Canst read, I mean,
Words fairly out and out?   Apothecaries

Adam Oehlenschläger

Never go farther in the common way
Than bare first syllables. That more than these
Are never seen upon their boxes, friend,
Has shortened many an honest fellow's days.

    Apoth. And who are you, that in your rusty cloak
Dare thus insult me with such saucy quips?
In my own shop I'll have fair words, I say.

    Alad. Fair words—that's my vocation; for my master
Is a grammarian. Does he not teach me
To trim and give a polish to my speech?
But if you really can read, if all
Your talk be not mere vaporing and wind,
Give me what's writ on this prescription here.

    Apoth. What do I see? You want this powder, this?

    Alad. And quickly too. Don't keep me waiting—come!

    Apoth. The foul fiend fly away with you, say I!

    Alad. The first of hucksters, thou, that ever sent
A customer to the devil.

    Apoth. No huckster I, and you no customer.

    Alad. Then what is your vocation? No huckster, eh?

    Apoth. You see in me a leech of skill, an artist,
A pharmacopolist, a man of science,
A doctor, a mediciner at least.

    Alad. And what, think you, am I?

    Apoth. A knave without the money for to buy
A drug so rare and of such potency.
What wouldst thou do with it? 'Tis poison.
Wouldst thou poison thyself?

    Alad. Myself? No—other folks.

    Apoth. How, other folks? Better and better still!
Come with me to the cadi.

    Alad. Tush! I have counsel for your ear.

Danish Wit and Humor

Apoth. Counsel for me?

Alad. Always hear people out before you judge.

Apoth. You're bent on poisoning?
Did you not say as much? If 'twere yourself,
It would not matter much. But other folks—
That was the word, and said without a blush!
And pray, sir, who may these same others be?
A pretty scrape you'd land me in! But whom
Would you send post-haste to the realm of shades?

Alad. Flies.

Apoth.   Flies?

Alad.   Wasps.

Apoth.   Wasps?

Alad. Gadflies—hm.

Apoth. Kill gadflies with a powder of such price?

Alad. Pish, man! I'm better off than you suppose.
It will not put me out so very much
To treat my flies to something savory.

(Gives him a piece of gold.)

Apoth. (*obsequiously*). This puts the case in quite another
    light.
(*Aside.*) Outside the man is rather rough, no doubt,
But he's a proper fellow at the core.
(*Aloud.*) That's quite another matter. Ah, dear sir,
You're not offended at my hasty words?
One must be circumspect in things like these;
One's bound to have a kind of conscience, eh?

Alad. Spoke like an oracle. But tell me, friend,
Suppose I'd kill a fly—I mean outright—
How much of this would do the business?

Apoth. That stands in mathematical relation,
If one may say so, to the insect's size.

Adam Oehlenschläger

Suppose it be an average sort of beast:
In sugared water drop the veriest grain,
And you will slay them by the thousand,
As with ass's jaw-bone Samson slew his foes.
>   (*Gives him the powder.*)

Alad.   But how, pray, if the fly were of your size?

Apoth.   How—my size?   There, you're at your quips
again!

You have some mischief in your thoughts, I swear.
As big as me?   Almighty Prophet! why,
The biggest horse-fly's not so big as that!

Alad.   You have a shrewd wit of your own, 'tis clear.
I do protest, 'tis flies I mean to kill;
But, as they're lodged within a mortal's head,
I must convey the powder through his lips.

Apoth.   Now, by the Prophet's grave, I'll give th' alarm!

Alad.   Indeed you won't!   You've wit enough to see
How easy 'twere for me to stop your mouth,
Should it grow clamorous, by a knock-down blow,
Or by this powder flirted down your throat.

Apoth.   A murrain on thee for a murderous knave!
Go, kill whome'er you please—I care not!
Kill flies, wasps, gadflies, gnats, philosophers,
Men and mosquitoes—anything you will,
So you but spare myself, my wife, and Hassan,
My little pet, my bandy-leggèd boy.

Alad.   Pah!   Fare you well—'tis but a jest, you know,
A harmless jest—no more.   (*Exit.*)

Apoth.   Who knows, now, what a rogue like this may do?
But he paid handsomely—and promptly too.
One must wink hard, and pocket many a slight,
Who would not lose his customers outright.—" *Aladdin.*"

Hans Christian Andersen

The Storks

ON the last house in a little village stood a stork's nest. The mother-stork sat in it with her four young ones, who stretched out their heads with the pointed black beaks, for their beaks had not yet turned red. A little way off stood the father-stork, all alone on the ridge of the roof, quite upright and stiff. He had drawn up one of his legs, so as not to be quite idle while he stood sentry. One would have thought he had been carved out of wood, so still did he stand. He thought, "It must look very grand, that my wife has a sentry standing by her nest. They can't tell that it is her husband. They certainly think I have been commanded to stand here. That looks so aristocratic!" And he went on standing on one leg.

Below, in the street, a whole crowd of children were playing; and when they caught sight of the storks, one of the boldest of the boys, and afterward all of them, sang the old verse about the storks. But they only sang it just as he could remember it:

> "Stork, stork, fly away!
> Stand not on one leg to-day.
> Thy dear wife is in the nest,
> Where she rocks her young to rest.
>
> The first, he will be hanged;
> The second will be hit;
> The third, he will be shot,
> And the fourth put on the spit."

126

"Just hear what those boys are saying!" said the little stork-children. "They say we are to be hanged and killed."

"You're not to care for that!" said the mother-stork. "Don't listen to it, and then it won't matter."

But the boys went on singing, and pointed at the storks mockingly with their fingers. Only one boy, whose name was Peter, declared that it was a sin to make a jest of animals, and he would not join in it at all.

The mother-stork comforted her children. "Don't you mind it at all," she said. "See how quiet your father stands, though it's only on one leg."

"We are very much afraid," said the young storks; and they drew their heads far back into the nest.

Now to-day, when the children came out again to play, and saw the storks, they sang their song:

> "The first, he will be hanged;
> The second will be hit——"

"Shall we be hanged and beaten?" asked the young storks.

"No, certainly not," replied the mother. "You shall learn to fly. I'll exercise you; then we shall fly out into the meadows and pay a visit to the frogs. They will bow before us in the water, and sing 'Croak! Croak!' and then we shall eat them up. That will be a real pleasure."

"And what then?" asked the young storks.

"Then all the storks will assemble, all that are here in the whole country, and the autumn exercises begin. Then one must fly well, for that is highly important; for whoever cannot fly properly will be thrust dead by the general's beak. So take care and learn well when the exercising begins."

"But then we shall be killed, as the boy says; and only listen, now they're singing again."

"Listen to me, and not to them," replied the mother-stork. "After the great review we shall fly away to the warm countries, far away from here, over mountains and forests. We shall fly to Egypt, where there are three covered houses of stone, which curl in a point and tower above the clouds; they are called pyramids, and are older than a stork can imagine. There is a river in that country which runs out of its bed, and then all the land is turned to mud. One walks about in the mud, and eats frogs."

"Oh-h!" cried the young ones.

"Yes. It is glorious there! One does nothing all day long but eat; and while we are so comfortable over there, here there is not a green leaf on the trees; here it is so cold that the clouds freeze to pieces, and fall down in little white rags!"

It was snow that she meant, but she could not explain it in any other way.

"And do the naughty boys freeze to pieces?" asked the young storks.

"No, they do not freeze to pieces; but they are not far from it, and must sit in a dark room and cower. You, on the other hand, can fly about in foreign lands, where there are flowers, and the sun shines warm."

Now some time had elapsed, and the nestlings had grown so large that they could stand upright in the nest and look far around; and the father-stork came every day with delicious frogs, little snakes, and all kinds of stork dainties as he found them. Oh, it looked funny when he performed feats before them! He laid his head quite back upon his tail, and clapped with his beak as if he had been a little clapper; and then he told them stories, all about the marshes.

"Listen! Now you must learn to fly," said the mother-stork one day; and all the four young ones had to go out on the ridge of the roof. Oh, how they tottered! How they balanced themselves with their wings, and yet they were nearly falling down!

"Only look at me," said the mother. "Thus you must hold your heads. Thus you must pitch your feet. One, two! One, two! That's what will help you on in the world."

Then she flew a little way, and the young ones made a little clumsy leap. Bump! there they lay, for their bodies were too heavy.

"I will not fly!" said one of the young storks, and crept back into the nest. "I don't care about getting to the warm countries."

"Do you want to freeze to death here when the winter comes? Are the boys to come and hang you, and singe you, and roast you? Now I'll call them."

"Oh, no!" cried the young stork, and hopped out on to the roof again like the rest.

On the third day they could actually fly a little, and then they thought they could also soar and hover in the air. They tried it, but—bump! down they tumbled, and they had to flap their wings again quickly enough. Now the boys came into the street again, and sang their song:

"Stork, stork, fly away!"

"Shall we fly down and pick their eyes out?" asked the young storks.

"No," replied the mother, "let them alone. Only listen to me; that's far more important. One, two, three! now we fly round to the right. One, two, three! now to the left, round the chimney. See, that was very good! The last kick with the feet was so neat and correct that you shall have permission to-morrow to fly with me to the marsh! Several nice stork families go there with their young; show them that mine are the nicest, and that you can start proudly; that looks well, and will get you consideration."

" But are we not to take revenge on the rude boys? " asked the young storks.

" Let them scream as much as they like. You will fly up to the clouds, and get to the land of the pyramids, when they will have to shiver, and not have a green leaf or a sweet apple."

" Yes, but we will revenge ourselves! " they whispered to one another; and then the exercising went on.

Among all the boys down in the street, the one most bent upon singing the teasing song was he who had begun it, and he was quite a little boy. He could hardly be more than six years old. The young storks certainly thought he was a hundred, for he was much bigger than their mother and father; and how should they know how old children and grown-up people can be? Their revenge was to come upon this boy, for it was he who had begun, and he always kept on. The young storks were very angry, and as they grew bigger they were less inclined to bear it; at last their mother had to promise them that they should be revenged, but not till the last day of their stay.

" We must first see how you behave at the grand review. If you get through badly, so that the general stabs you through the chest with his beak, the boys will be right, at least, in one way. Let us see."

" Yes, you shall see! " cried the young storks; and then they took all imaginable pains. They practised every day, and flew so neatly and so lightly that it was a pleasure to see them.

Now the autumn came on; all the storks began to assemble, to fly away to the warm countries while it is winter here. That *was* a review. They had to fly over forests and villages, to show how well they could soar, for it was a long journey they had before them. The young storks did their part so well that they got, as a mark, "Remarkably well, with frogs and snakes." That was the highest mark; and they might eat the frogs and snakes; and that is what they did.

"Now we will be revenged!" they said.

"Yes, certainly," said the mother-stork. "What I have thought of will be the best. I know the pond in which all the little mortals lie till the stork comes and brings them to their parents. The pretty little babies lie there and dream so sweetly as they never dream afterward. All parents are glad to have such a child, and all children want to have a sister or a brother. Now we will fly to the pond, and bring one for each of the children who have not sung the naughty song and laughed at the storks."

"But he who began to sing—that naughty, ugly boy!" screamed the young storks; "what shall we do with him?"

"There is a little dead child in the pond, one that has dreamed itself to death; we will bring that for him. Then he will cry because we have brought him a little dead brother. But that good boy—you have not forgotten him, the one who said, 'It is wrong to laugh at animals!'—for him we will bring a brother and a sister too. And as his name is Peter, all of you shall be called Peter too."

And it was done as she said; all the storks were named Peter, and so they are all called even now.—"*Fairy Tales.*"

The Lovers

A WHIP-TOP and a little ball were together in a drawer among some other toys; and the top said to the ball, " Shall we not be bridegroom and bride, as we live together in the same box ? "

But the ball, which had a coat of morocco leather, and was just as conceited as any fine lady, would make no answer to such a proposal.

Next day the little boy came to whom the toys belonged; he painted the top red and yellow, and hammered a brass nail into it; and it looked splendid when the top turned round !

" Look at me ! " he cried to the ball. " What do you say now? Shall we not be engaged to each other? We suit one another so well ! You jump, and I dance ! No one could be happier than we two should be."

" Indeed ! Do you think so ? " replied the little ball. " Perhaps you do not know my papa and mama were morocco slippers, and that I have a Spanish cork inside me ? "

" Yes, but I am made of mahogany," said the top; " and the mayor himself turned me. He has a turning-lathe of his own, and it amuses him greatly."

" Can I depend upon that ? " asked the little ball.

" May I never be whipped again if it is not true ! " replied the top.

" You can speak well for yourself," observed the ball, " but I cannot grant your request. I am as good as engaged to a swallow; every time I leap up into the air she puts her head out of her nest and says, 'Will you?' And now I have silently said 'Yes,' and that is as good as half engaged. But I promise I will never forget you."

"Yes, a lot of good that will be!" said the top.

And they spoke no more to each other.

The next day the ball was taken out by the boy. The top saw how it flew high into the air, like a bird; at last one could no longer see it. Each time it came back again, but gave a high leap when it touched the earth, and that was done either from its longing to mount up again, or because it had a Spanish cork in its body. But the ninth time the little ball remained absent, and did not come back again; and the boy sought and sought, but it was gone.

"I know very well where it is!" sighed the top. "It is in the swallow's nest, and has married the swallow."

The more the top thought of this the more it longed for the ball. Just because it could not get the ball, its love increased; and the fact that the ball had chosen another formed a peculiar feature in the case. So the top danced round and hummed, but always thought of the little ball, which became more and more beautiful in his fancy. Thus several years went by, and now it was an old love.

And the top was no longer young! But one day he was gilt all over; never had he looked so handsome; he was now a golden top, and sprang till he hummed again. Yes, that was something worth seeing! But all at once he sprang up too high, and—he was gone.

They looked and looked, even in the cellar, but he was not to be found. Where could he be?

He had jumped into the dust-box, where all kinds of things were lying: cabbage-stalks, sweepings, and rubbish that had fallen down from the roof.

" Here's a nice place to lie in! The gilding will soon leave me here. Among what a rabble have I alighted!"

And then he looked sideways at a long, leafless cabbage-stump, and at a curious round thing that looked like an old apple; but it was not an apple—it was an old ball, which had lain for years in the gutter on the roof, and was quite saturated with water.

" Thank goodness, here comes one of us, with whom one can talk!" said the little ball, and looked at the gilt top. " I am really morocco, worked by maiden's hands, and have a Spanish cork within me; but no one would think it, to look at me. I was very nearly marrying a swallow, but I fell into the gutter on the roof, and have lain there full five years, and become quite wet through. You may believe me; that's a long time for a young girl."

But the top said nothing. He thought of his old love; and the more he heard, the clearer it became to him that this was she.

Then came the servant-girl, and wanted to turn out the dust-box.

" Ah, there's a gilt top!" she cried.

And so the top was brought again to notice an honor, but nothing was heard of the little ball. And the top spoke no more of his old love; for that dies away when the beloved object has lain for five years in a roof gutter and got wet through. Yes, one does not know her again when one meets her in the dust-box.—" *Fairy Tales.*"

Hans Christian Andersen

Good Humor

My father left me the best inheritance, to wit, good humor.
And who was my father? Why, that has nothing to do with
the humor. He was lively and stout, round and fat; and his
outer and inner man was in direct contradiction to his calling.
And pray what was he by profession and calling in civil
society? Yes, if this were to be written down and printed
in the very beginning of a book, it is probable that many
when they read it would lay the book aside, and say, "It
looks so uncomfortable; I don't like anything of that sort."
And yet my father was neither a horse-slaughterer nor an
executioner; on the contrary, his office placed him at the
head of the most respectable gentry of the town; and he held
his place by right, for it was his right place. He had to go
first before the bishop even, and before the princes of the
blood. He always went first—for he was the driver of the
hearse!

There, now it's out! And I will confess that when people
saw my father sitting perched up on the omnibus of death,
dressed in his long, wide, black cloak, and with his black-
bordered, three-cornered hat on his head—and then his face,
exactly as the sun is drawn, round and jocund—it was difficult for them to think of the grave and of sorrow. The face
said, "It doesn't matter—it doesn't matter; it will be better
than you think."

You see I have inherited my good humor from him, and
also the habit of going often to the churchyard, which is a
good thing to do if it be done in the right spirit; and then I
take in the *Intelligencer,* just as he used to do.

Danish Wit and Humor

I am not quite young. I have neither wife, nor children, nor a library; but, as aforesaid, I take in the *Intelligencer,* and that's my favorite newspaper, as it was also my father's. It is very useful, and contains everything that a man needs to know—such as who preaches in the church, and the new books. And then, what a lot of charity, and what a number of innocent, harmless verses are found in it! Advertisements for husbands and wives, and requests for interviews—all quite simple and natural. Certainly, one may live merrily and be contentedly buried if one takes in the *Intelligencer.* And as a concluding advantage, by the end of his life a man will have such a capital store of paper, that he may use it as a soft bed, unless he prefers to rest upon wood shavings.

The newspaper and my walk to the churchyard were always my most exciting occupations; they were like bathing-places for my good humor.

The newspaper every one can read for himself. But please come with me to the churchyard; let us wander there, where the sun shines and the trees grow green. Each of the narrow houses is like a closed book, with the back placed uppermost, so that one can only read the title and judge what the book contains, but can tell nothing about it. But I know something about them. I heard it from my father, or found it out myself. I have it all down in my record, that I wrote out for my own use and pleasure. All that lie here, and a few more, too, are chronicled in it.

Now we are in the churchyard.

Here, behind the white railing, where once a rose-tree grew —it is gone now, but a little evergreen from the next grave stretches out its green fingers to make a show—there rests a very unhappy man; and yet, when he lived, he was in what

they call a good position. He had enough to live upon, and
something over; but worldly cares, or, to speak more correctly, his great artistic taste, weighed heavily upon him.
If in the evening he sat in the theater to enjoy himself thoroughly, he would be quite annoyed if the machinist had put
too strong a light into one side of the moon, or if the sky-
pieces hung down over the scenes when they ought to have
hung behind them, or when a palm-tree was introduced into
a scene representing the Berlin Zoological Gardens, or a
cactus in a view of the Tyrol, or a beech-tree in the far north
of Norway. As if that was of any consequence. Is it not
quite immaterial? Who would fidget about such a trifle?
It's only make-believe, after all, and every one is expected to
be amused. Then sometimes the public applauded too much
to suit his taste, and sometimes too little. "They're like wet
wood this evening," he would say; "they won't kindle at
all!" And then he would look about to see what kind of
people they were; and sometimes he would find them laughing at the wrong time, when they ought not to have laughed,
and that vexed him; and he fretted and was an unhappy man,
and at last fretted himself into his grave.

Here rests a very happy man; that is to say, a very grand
man. He was of high birth, and that was lucky for him, for
otherwise he would never have been anything worth speaking
of; and Nature orders all that very wisely, so that it's quite
charming when we think of it. He used to go about in a
coat embroidered back and front, and appeared in the saloons
of society just like one of those costly, pearl-embroidered
bell-pulls which have always a good, thick, serviceable cord
behind them to do the work. He likewise had a good stout
cord behind him in the shape of a substitute, who did his
duty, and who still continues to do it behind another em-

broidered bell-pull. Everything is so nicely managed, it's enough to put one into a good humor.

Here rests—well, it's a very mournful reflection—here rests a man who spent sixty-seven years considering how he should get a good idea. The sole object of his life was to say a good thing, and at last he felt convinced in his own mind that he had got one; was so glad of it that he died of pure joy at having caught an idea at last. Nobody derived any benefit from it, and nobody even heard what the good thing was. Now, I can fancy that this same good thing won't let him lie quiet in his grave; for let us suppose that it is a good thing which can only be brought out at breakfast if it is to make an effect, and that he, according to the received opinion concerning ghosts, can only rise and walk at midnight. Why, then the good thing would not suit the time, and the man must carry his good idea down with him again. What an unhappy man he must be!

Here rests a remarkably stingy woman. During her lifetime she used to get up at night and mew, so that the neighbors might think she kept a cat—she was so remarkably stingy.

Here is a maiden of another kind. When the canary-bird of the heart begins to chirp, reason puts her fingers in her ears. The maiden was going to be married, but— Well, it's an every-day story, and we will let the dead rest.

Here sleeps a widow, who carried melody in her mouth and gall in her heart. She used to go out for prey in the families round about; and the prey she hunted was her neighbors' faults, and she was an indefatigable hunter.

Here's a family sepulcher. Every member of this family held so firmly to the opinions of the rest, that if all the world, and the newspapers into the bargain, said of a certain thing it is so and so, and the little boy came home from school and said, "I've learned it thus and thus," they declared his opinion to be the only true one, because he belonged to the family. And it is an acknowledged fact, that if the yard cock of the family crowed at midnight, they would declare it was morning, though the watchmen and all the clocks in the city were crying out that it was twelve o'clock at night.

The great poet Goethe concludes his *Faust* with the words "May be continued"; and our wanderings in the churchyard may be continued too. If any of my friends, or my enemies, get too fast for me, I go out to my favorite spot, and select a mound, and bury him or her there—bury that person who is yet alive; and there those I bury must stay till they come back as new and improved characters. I inscribe their life and their deeds, looked at in my fashion, in my record; and that's what all people ought to do. They ought not to be vexed when any one goes on ridiculously, but bury him directly, and maintain their good humor, and keep to the *Intelligencer,* which is often a book written by the people with its hand guided.

When the time comes for me to be bound with my history in the boards of the grave, I hope they will put up as my epitaph, "A good-humored one."—"*Essays.*"

A Night in a Stage-Coach

THE last railway-station is at Perpignan, but it is only a few hours' journey from that place into Spain. The said journey had been described to me as very terrible. The stage-coaches were represented as vehicles specially designed for torture—great, heavy omnibuses, with only one door at the side, so that there was no way of getting out if there was an upset, which occurred with fatal regularity. Protestants were despised in this part of the country, and persecuted as if they were ungodly heathens, so I was told; travelers were constantly being attacked and robbed by armed brigands; and, as for the food, none of it was eatable. I had heard and read all this, and now I was to experience it.

The stage-coach was to leave Perpignan at three o'clock in the morning. To start at three means getting up at two; and if you are to rise as early as that, you might as well not go to bed at all. I lay down, nevertheless, and managed to obtain a few scattered winks, in the intervals between which I looked at my watch or stared at the sky. Finally, at half past two, I waked up the man who was to have called me, and having consumed a glass of cold water— the only breakfast available at that hour—I made my way to the starting-place. A lantern on a barrel disclosed six stage-coaches jammed closely together. There was not much room for the numbers who intended to go. The travelers appeared one by one. Not a soul knew another; not a word was spoken. One sat down on an empty wooden box, another on a trunk, another stumbled about among the harness, and a good many were lost to view in dark corners. The coaches were loaded with luggage and human freight, while twelve horses with jingling bells were fastened to each. I secured a place in the inner compartment, with a Spanish lady and her daughter, both of them wearing enormous crinolines. If they had gone to Skagen, the mother alone would have covered the whole of the northern part of that promontory. I felt as if I were sitting beside a balloon that was being inflated.

Hans Christian Andersen

The postilions cracked their whips, and off we went, swinging from side to side in the narrow streets. We passed over the drawbridge and through the fortifications—the sort of scenery you would expect in a melodrama of the Middle Ages. After a time we got out upon the open highroad. The señora was asleep. She was probably dreaming of her beautiful Spain, where she once had loved and been loved—seeing that she had a daughter. I, too, dreamed of Spain—with my eyes wide open, wondering what was in store for me there. The daughter neither slept nor dreamed. All her attention seemed to be centered upon a knitted bag which she held in her lap, and which she was perpetually lifting up and putting down again.

The bag began to worry me (I had got used to the crinoline), and I found myself speculating on its possible contents. I imagined that the thing in it prized most highly was neither gold nor silver money, nor jewelry, nor any fine Parisian frills to be smuggled across the frontier. No; my poetical eye penetrated the secret of the bag, and I saw there a man, a handsome man, on a photograph, all spick and span, from his frizzled curls to the tips of his shining boots, though in his proper person he was no doubt still more beautiful. I interfered with him, being so close to his lady-love, and he interfered with me in his case—that ponderous bag, which now bumped against my stomach and now against my chest, as the Spanish damsel, clinging to her treasure, assumed various plastic attitudes. Mama meanwhile was sleeping soundly, and executing nasal runs and trills such as sleepers give forth when it is inconvenient to put any restraint on their breathing.

A star in the west, out over the sea, shone so wonderfully clearly, and looked so large, that I was uncertain whether I saw a star or a lighthouse. I had long been wishing to begin a conversation with the young Spaniard, hoping that my stock of Spanish, which consisted in some of the commonest expressions, would come out in the right order, and relying upon my talent for that sort of enterprise. But what a lighthouse might be in Spanish I had no idea, and so I commenced with what I did know—"Estrella." The word took like a spark, and kindled the fire of eloquence in the Spanish girl. She talked and she talked. Words flowed from her lips like the waters spouting from a fountain. But not a thing did I understand. Presently day dawned, and I beheld the sea. I then exclaimed, " El mar ! " Thereupon ensued another attempt at conversation. " Inglés ? " she asked. " Danés ! " I replied, and we began to chat—that is to say, I would give a cue, and she would spin out the thread of the discourse. I said, " La poesia de la España—Cervantes, Calderon, Moreto ! " All I did was to mention names, and as each name was uttered her animation increased, so that her mama was at length awakened, when her daughter informed her that I had been talking in the most interesting manner about Spanish literature. But it was herself who had done the talking; I did not know how.

—" *Travels in Spain.*"

Norwegian Wit and Humor

Henrik Ibsen

Scene from "An Enemy of the People."

DR. STOCKMANN, *Medical Officer of the Baths;* MRS. STOCK-
MANN, *his Wife;* BURGOMASTER STOCKMANN, *his
Brother;* HOVSTAD, *Editor of the " People's Messenger";*
BILLING, HOVSTAD'S *Assistant;* ASLAKSEN, *Owner of a
Printing-House; Assembly of Townsfolk.*

Aslak. Burgomaster Stockmann will address the meeting.

Burg. On account of my close relationship—of which you
are probably aware—to the present medical officer of the
baths, I should have preferred not to speak here this evening; but my position with regard to the baths, and my care
for the most important interests of this town, force me to
move a resolution. I may doubtless assume that not a single
citizen here present thinks it desirable that untrustworthy
and exaggerated statements should get abroad as to the sani-
tary condition of the baths, and of our town. I therefore beg
to move, " That this meeting declines to hear the proposed
lecture or speech on the subject by the medical officer of the
baths." But I must preface that in my statement in the
People's Messenger I have made the public acquainted with
the essential facts, so that all well-disposed citizens can
easily draw their own conclusions. From that statement you
will see that the medical officer's proposal, besides amount-
ing to a vote of censure against the leading men of the

town, at bottom only means saddling the ratepayers with an unnecessary expense of at least a hundred thousand crowns.

. . . .

Aslak. I will now put the burgomaster's resolution to the vote.

Dr. Stock. It's not necessary. I sha'n't say anything this evening of all the filth at the baths. No; you shall hear something quite different! I am about to make great revelations, fellow citizens! I am going to announce to you a far more important discovery than the trifling fact that our water-works are poisoned, and that our health-resort is built on pestilential ground.

Many Voices (shouting). Don't speak about the baths! We won't listen to that! No more of that!

Dr. Stock. I have said I would speak of the great discovery I have made within the last few days—the discovery that all our sources of spiritual life are poisoned, and that our whole society rests upon a pestilential basis of falsehood.

Several Voices (in astonishment, and half aloud). What's he saying?

Burg. Such an insinuation——

Aslak. (with his hand on the bell). I must call upon the speaker to moderate his expressions.

Dr. Stock. I have loved my native town as dearly as man could love the home of his childhood. I was young when I left our town, and distance, homesickness, and memory threw, as it were, a glamor over the place and its people. *(Some clapping and shouts of approval.)* Then for years I was imprisoned in a horrible hole, far away in the north.

Henrik Ibsen

As I went about among the people scattered here and there over the stony wilderness, it seemed to me, many a time, that these poor degraded creatures ought to have had a cattle-doctor to attend them, rather than a man like me.

(*Murmurs in the room.*)

Bill. (*laying down his pen*). Strike me dead if I've ever heard——

Hov. What an insult to a worthy peasantry!

Dr. Stock. Wait a moment! I don't think any one can reproach me with forgetting my native town up there. I sat brooding like an eider-duck, and what I hatched was— the plan of the baths. (*Applause and interruptions.*) And when, at last, fate ordered things so happily that I could come home again, then, fellow citizens, it seemed to me that I hadn't another desire in the world. Yes, one desire I had: an eager, constant, burning desire to be of service to my birthplace, and to its people.

Burg. A strange method to select—hm!

Dr. Stock. So I went about reveling in my happy illusions. But yesterday morning—no, it was really two nights ago— my mind's eyes were opened wide, and the first thing I saw was the extraordinary stupidity of the authorities——

(*Noise, cries, and laughter.* MRS. STOCKMANN *coughs emphatically.*)

Burg. Mr. Chairman!

Aslak. (*ringing his bell*). In virtue of my position——

Dr. Stock. It's petty to catch me up on a word, Mr. Aslaksen. I only meant that I became alive to the extraordinary muddle the leading men had been guilty of down at the baths. I detest leading men; I've seen enough of them in my time. They're like goats in a young plantation: they do harm everywhere; they block the path of a free man wherever he turns, and I should be glad if we could exterminate them like other noxious animals——

(Uproar in the room.)

Burg. Mr. Chairman, are such expressions permissible?

Aslak. (*with his hand on the bell*). Dr. Stockmann——

Dr. Stock. I can't conceive how it is that I've only now seen through these gentry; for haven't I had a magnificent example before my eyes here every day—my brother Peter —slow of understanding, tenacious in prejudice——

(Laughter, noise, and whistling. MRS. STOCKMANN *coughs.* ASLAKSEN *rings violently.)*

Well, fellow citizens, I'll say no more about our leading men. If any one imagines, from what I've just said, that I want to make short work of these gentlemen to-night, he's mistaken—altogether mistaken; for I cherish the comforting belief that these laggards, these relics of a decaying order of thought, are diligently cutting their own throats. They need no doctor to hasten their end. And these are not the people that constitute the most serious danger to society; it is not they who are most active in poisoning our spiritual life and making a plague-spot of the ground beneath our feet; it is not they who are the most dangerous enemies of truth and freedom in our society.

Cries from all sides. Who, then? Who is it? Name! Name!

Dr. Stock. Yes, you may be sure I'll name them; for *this* is the great discovery I made yesterday! (*In a louder tone.*) The most dangerous foe to truth and freedom in our midst is the compact majority. Yes, it's the confounded, compact, liberal majority! There, I've told you!

(Immense disturbance in the room. Most of the au- dience are shouting, stamping, and whistling. MRS.

Henrik Ibsen

STOCKMANN *rises nervously.* ASLAKSEN *rings the bell and calls for order.* HOVSTAD *and* BILLING *both speak, but neither can be heard. At last quiet is restored.*)

Aslak. I request the speaker to withdraw his ill-considered expressions.

Dr. Stock. Never, Mr. Aslaksen! For it's this very majority that robs me of my freedom, and wants to forbid me to speak the truth.

Hov. Right is always on the side of the majority.

Bill. Yes, and truth, too, strike me dead!

Dr. Stock. The majority is never right! Never, I say! That's one of the social lies a free, thinking man is bound to rebel against. Who make up the majority in any given country? Is it the wise men, or the fools? I think we must agree that the fools are in a terrible, overwhelming majority, all the wide world over. But how the deuce can it ever be right for the fools to rule over the wise men? (*Noise and shouts.*) Yes, yes, you can shout me down, but you cannot gainsay me. The majority has might, unhappily, but right it has not. I and the few, the individuals, are right. The minority is always right! (*Renewed disturbance.*)

Hov. Ha-ha! So Dr. Stockmann has turned aristocrat since the day before yesterday.

Dr. Stock. I'm going to revolt against the lie that truth resides in the majority! What sort of truths do the majority rally round? Truths that are decrepit with age. When a truth is so old as that it's in a fair way to become a lie, gentlemen. (*Laughter and jeers.*) Yes, yes, you may believe me or not, as you please; but truths are by no means the wiry Methuselahs some people think them. A normally constituted truth lives, let me say, as a rule, seventeen or

147

eighteen years; at the outside twenty—seldom longer. And truths so stricken in years are always shockingly thin; yet it's not till then that the majority takes them up, and recommends them to society as wholesome food. I can assure you there's not much nutriment in that sort of fare; you may take my word as a doctor for that. All these majority truths are like last year's salt pork; they're like rancid, moldy ham, producing all the moral scurvy that devastates society.

Aslak. It seems to me that the honorable speaker is wandering rather far from the subject.

Burg. I beg to indorse the chairman's remark.

Dr. Stock. Why, you're surely mad, Peter! I'm keeping as closely to my text as I possibly can, for my text is just this: that the masses, the majority, that confounded compact majority—it's that, I say, that's poisoning our spiritual life at its source, and making a plague-spot of the ground beneath our feet!

Hov. And you make this charge against the great, independent majority, just because they're sensible enough to accept only certain and acknowledged truths?

Dr. Stock. Ah, my dear Mr. Hovstad, don't talk about certain truths! The truths acknowledged by the masses, the multitude, were certain truths to the vanguard in our grandfathers' days. We, the vanguard of to-day, don't acknowledge them any longer; and I don't believe there's any other certain truth but this: that no society can live a healthy life upon such old, marrowless truths as these!

Hov. But instead of all this vague talk, suppose you were to give us some specimens of these old marrowless truths that we're living upon. (*Approval from several quarters.*)

Dr. Stock. Oh, I can't go over the whole rubbish-heap;

so, for the present, I'll keep to one acknowledged truth, which is a hideous lie at bottom, but which Mr. Hovstad, and the *Messenger,* and all adherents of the *Messenger,* live on nevertheless.

Hov. And that is——

Dr. Stock. That is the doctrine you've inherited from our forefathers, and go on heedlessly proclaiming far and wide: the doctrine that the multitude, the vulgar herd, the masses, are the pith of the people; that they *are* the people; that the common man, the ignorant, undeveloped member of society, has the same right to condemn and to sanction, to counsel and to govern, as the intellectually distinguished few.

Bill. Well, now, strike me dead——

Hov. (*shouting at the same time*). Citizens, please note that!

Angry Voices. Ho-ho! Aren't we the people? Is it only the grand folks that are to govern?

A Working Man. Turn out the fellow that talks like that!

Others. Turn him out!

A Citizen (*shouting*). Now for your horn, Evensen.

(*The deep notes of a horn are heard; whistling, and terrific noise in the room.*)

Dr. Stock. (*when the noise has somewhat subsided*). Now do be reasonable! Can't you bear to hear the voice of truth for once? I don't ask you all to agree with me straight away. But I certainly should have thought that Mr. Hovstad would have backed me up, when he'd collected himself a bit. Mr. Hovstad calls himself a freethinker——

Several Voices (*subdued and wondering*). Freethinker, did he say? What, Mr. Hovstad a freethinker?

Hov. (*shouting*). Prove it, Dr. Stockmann! When have I said so in print?

Norwegian Wit and Humor

Dr. Stock. (*reflecting*). No, on my soul you're right there; you've never had the frankness to do that. Well, I won't get you into a scrape, Mr. Hovstad. Let me be the free-thinker, then. And now I'll make it clear to you all, and on scientific grounds, that the *Messenger* is leading you shamefully by the nose, when it tells you that you, the masses, the crowd, are the true pith of the people. You see that's only a newspaper lie. The masses are nothing but the raw material that must be fashioned into the people. (*Murmurs, laughter, and disturbance in the room.*) Is it not so with all other living creatures? What a difference between a cultivated and an uncultivated breed of animals! Only look at a common barn-door hen. What meat do you get from such a skinny carcass? Not much, I can tell you. And what sort of eggs does she lay? A decent crow or raven can lay nearly as good. Then take a cultivated Spanish or Japanese hen, or take a fine pheasant or turkey—ah, then you'll see the difference! And now look at the dog, our near relation. Think first of an ordinary vulgar cur—I mean one of those wretched, ragged, low mongrels that haunt the gutters and soil the foot-walks. Then place such a mongrel by the side of a poodle-dog, descended through many generations from an aristocratic strain, who has lived on delicate food, and has heard harmonious voices and music. Do you think the brain of the poodle hasn't developed quite differently from that of the mongrel? Yes, you may be sure it has. It's well-bred poodle-pups like this that jugglers train to perform the most extraordinary tricks. A common peasant cur could never learn anything of the sort—not if he tried till doomsday.

(*Noise and laughter are heard all round.*)

A Citizen (*shouting*). Do you want to make dogs of us now?

Henrik Ibsen

Another Man. We're not animals, doctor.

Dr. Stock. Yes, on my soul, but we are animals, my good sir! We're one and all of us animals, whether we like it or not. But truly there aren't many aristocratic animals among us. Ah, there's a terrible difference between men-poodles and men-mongrels! And the ridiculous part of it is, that Mr. Hovstad quite agrees with me so long as it's four-legged animals we're talking of——

Hov. Oh, let them alone!

Dr. Stock. All right; but so soon as I apply the law to two-legged animals, Mr. Hovstad stops short; then he daren't hold his own opinions or think out his own thoughts; then he turns all his knowledge topsyturvy, and proclaims in the *People's Messenger* that barn-door hens and gutter mongrels are precisely the finest specimens in the menagerie. But that's always the way, so long as you haven't worked the commonness out of your system, and fought your way up to spiritual distinction.

Hov. I make no pretensions to any sort of distinction. I come of simple peasant stock, and I'm proud that my root lies deep down among the common people, who are now being jeered at.

Several Workmen. Hurrah for Hovstad! Hurrah! Hurrah!

Dr. Stock. The sort of common people I'm speaking of are not found among the lower classes alone; they crawl and swarm all around us—up to the very summits of society. Just look at your own smug, respectable burgomaster! Why, my brother Peter belongs as clearly to the common people as any man that walks on two legs——

(*Laughter and hisses.*)

Burg. I protest against such personalities.

151

Norwegian Wit and Humor

Dr. Stock. ——and that not because, like myself, he's descended from a good-for-nothing old pirate from Pomerania, or thereabout—for that's our ancestry——

Burg. An absurd tradition! Utterly groundless!

Dr. Stock. ——but he is so because he thinks the thoughts and holds the opinions of his official superiors. Men who do that belong, intellectually speaking, to the mob; and that's why my distinguished brother Peter is at bottom so undistinguished—and consequently so illiberal.

Burg. Mr. Chairman——

Hov. So the distinguished people in this country are the liberals? That's quite a new light on the subject.

(*Laughter.*)

Dr. Stock. Yes, that's part of my new discovery. And this, too, follows, that liberality of thought is almost precisely the same thing as morality. Therefore I say it's altogether unpardonable of the *Messenger* to proclaim day after day the false doctrine that it's the masses, the multitude, the compact majority, that monopolize liberality and morality; and that vice and corruption and all sorts of spiritual uncleanness ooze out of culture, as all that filth oozes down to the baths from the Mill Dale tan-works! (*Noise and interruptions.* Dr. Stockmann *goes on imperturbably, smiling in his eagerness.*) And yet this same *Messenger* can preach about raising the masses and the multitude to a higher level of life! Why, deuce take it, if the *Messenger's* own doctrine holds good, the elevation of the masses would simply mean hurling them into destruction. But, happily, it's only an old traditional lie that culture demoralizes. No, it's stupidity, poverty, the ugliness of life, that do the devil's work! In a house that isn't aired and swept every day—my wife

Henrik Ibsen

Katrine maintains that the floors ought to be scrubbed too, but we can't discuss that now—well, in such a house, I say, within two or three years people lose the power of thinking or acting morally. Lack of oxygen enervates the conscience. And there seems to be precious little oxygen in many and many a house in this town, since the whole compact majority is unscrupulous enough to want to found its future upon a quagmire of lies and fraud.

Aslak. I cannot allow so gross an insult to be leveled against the whole body of citizens.

A Gentleman. I move that the chairman order the speaker to sit down.

Eager Voices. Yes, yes, that's right! Sit down! Sit down!

Dr. Stock. Then I'll proclaim the truth at every street corner! I'll write to newspapers in other towns! The whole land shall know how things go on here!

Hov. It would almost seem as if the doctor wanted to ruin the town.

Dr. Stock. Yes, I love my native town so well, I would rather ruin it than see it flourishing upon a lie.

Aslak. That's putting it strongly.

(*Noise and whistling.* Mrs. STOCKMANN *coughs in vain; the* DOCTOR *does not heed her.*)

Hov. (*shouting amid the tumult*). The man who would ruin a whole community must be an enemy to his fellow citizens!

Dr. Stock. (*with growing excitement*). What does it matter if a lying community is ruined? It should be leveled to the ground, I say! All men who live upon lies should be exterminated like vermin! You'll poison the whole country

153

in time; you'll bring it to such a pass that the whole country will deserve to perish. And if it ever comes to that, I shall say, from the bottom of my heart: Perish the country! Perish all its people!

A Man (*in the crowd*). Why, he talks like a regular enemy of the people!

Bill. Strike me dead, but there spoke the people's voice!

The Whole Assembly (*shouting*). Yes! Yes! Yes! He's an enemy of the people! He hates his country! He hates the people!

Aslak. Both as a citizen of this town and as a man, I am deeply shocked at what I have here had to listen to. Dr. Stockmann has unmasked himself in a manner I should never have dreamed of. I am reluctantly forced to subscribe to the opinion just expressed by some worthy citizens, and I think we ought to formulate this opinion in a resolution. I therefore beg to move, " That this meeting declares the medical officer of the baths, Dr. Thomas Stockmann, to be an enemy of the people."

(*Thunders of applause and cheers. Many form a circle round the* Doctor *and hoot at him.*)

Dr. Stock. (*to the people hooting*). Ah, fools that you are! I tell you that——

Aslak. (*ringing*). The doctor is out of order in speaking. A formal vote must be taken; but out of consideration for personal feelings, it will be taken in writing and without names. Have you any blank paper, Mr. Billing?

Bill. Here's both blue and white paper——

Aslak. That'll do; we can manage more quickly this way. Tear it up. That's it. (*To the meeting.*) Blue means no, white means yes. I myself will go round and collect the votes.

154

Henrik Ibsen

(*The* BURGOMASTER *leaves the room.* ASLAKSEN *and a few others go round with pieces of paper in hats.*)

. . . .

Aslak. With the exception of one intoxicated person, this meeting of citizens declares the medical officer of the baths, Dr. Thomas Stockmann, to be an enemy of the people. (*Cheers and applause.*) Three cheers for our fine old municipality! (*Cheers.*) Three cheers for our able and energetic burgomaster, who has so loyally put aside the claims of kindred! (*Cheers.*) The meeting is dissolved.

Jonas Lie

The Snake in the Schoolroom

SCHULTHEISS strutted up and down the schoolroom with his brows knit. He was staring at his feet, of which he was exceedingly proud. He put one before the other with precision and elegance, step by step, and whenever he turned round made a deep bend of the knees, answering to the intellectual strain he was undergoing. His gait increased while his excitement grew. Suddenly he stopped, resuming thus, with a beaming, self-confident smile:

" ' The History of the Spinning-Wheel '—that is the title of the work I intend to write, in several volumes. What has there not been spun out of the spinning-wheel? The men have gone through the thread-loop like dots of wool. But I mean—hm—that this romantic sort of stuff about woman I shall leave to the petty scribblers. As for me, I— I "—he ejaculated passionately, until his voice became a squeak—" I will light a firebrand, show up the slave who is being bought and sold, who is chained to the spinning-wheel. And then," looking solemnly at Minka, " begins the struggle for liberty. It is a highly complicated and delicate subject, which only a genius with the most penetrating powers of psychological analysis can unravel in all its details. Such a man must know the female heart to the core—yes, to the very core, I tell you! "

At this moment Arnt snatched the master's handkerchief, which was protruding from the pocket of his coat tail.

" But when my pen is once let loose," shouted the pedagogue, waving and flourishing his right arm so that his bare, bony wrist could be seen far out of his sleeve, " I will make revelations—ha, *such* revelations! "

Just then Arnt partly pulled down the handkerchief, which hung downward like a tail.

" I will lay bare all her weapons—the whole arsenal! Step by step will I follow up her wretched career, and prove how her secret yet constant opposition and intrigue against the lord of creation has turned her best feelings into sharply pointed, poisoned weapons, into the most wily allurements, and has made her mistress of all the most treacherous arts, and has perfected her in deceit and duplicity, and has changed her whole nature! Yes, changed her whole nature! "

He shot a fiery glance at Minka.

" She plays and coquets with man," declaimed the wrought-up Schultheiss, " as selfishly, coldly, and cruelly as the cat with the mouse. She sits "—he put on a bland smile —" by the trap, bewitchingly flattering and enticing him; and when the fool has jumped into it "—a contemptuous kick at the air illustrated his meaning—" he surrenders his very life, while she weeps irresistible, heartrending tears! "

He paced rapidly up and down, while the handkerchief wagged to and fro behind him.

" She has turned into the world's great impostor, whose satanic passion it is to allure and destroy! She is a dangerous creature, I say, a venomous, creeping thing, sparkling with a thousand colors "—his voice grew sarcastic—" to be watched with suspicion, like a snake which you think you have tamed."

" Hee-hee-hee! Look at the snake! " laughed the scholars, while Ole was at that moment trying to abstract the handkerchief altogether from the schoolmaster's pocket.

Schultheiss assumed a straddling position, and began rocking back and forth, with his head thrown back and his eyes fixed upon the ceiling. The "snake" was now hanging far down, and the pupils were watching it with breathless suspense.

"I have just exhibited a terrible picture to you," said Schultheiss, taking a deep breath, and turning toward Minka.

"What did you say? I beg your pardon," remarked the girl as she looked up at him with an innocent, preoccupied air. "I was busy with my exercise."

A deadly pallor suddenly overspread his face; all his grandeur seemed to shrivel up and disappear; there was nothing but a nervous, fussy little figure left. He coughed, and began again with a stutter:

"I had n-next inten-ten-ded to represent w-woman when her sense of dignity is awakened, when her grand and noble struggle——"

"Hee-hee-hee! The snake! There lies the snake!" giggled all the boys in a fit of uncontrollable mirth.

Schultheiss looked about bewildered.

"There it is!" exclaimed Berthea obligingly, calling his attention to it where it lay on the floor.

The master hastily picked up the handkerchief, stuffed it into his pocket, snatched up a book, and flurriedly passed on to another lesson.—"*Niobe.*"

Swedish Wit and Humor

August Strindberg

Love and Bread

FALK, the royal secretary, was certainly not informed as to the market-price of wheat when he rode out to the major's to ask his daughter's hand.

" I love Louisa," began the secretary.

" How much do you earn? " asked the old man.

" A trifle less than twelve hundred crowns. But then we love each other so devotedly, dear uncle."

" That does not concern me. Twelve hundred crowns is not enough."

" I have some extra work besides. Louisa knows my heart."

" Don't speak so childishly! How much do you earn by this extra work? "

" We met first at Boo, on the island Lidingö."

" How much do you earn outside? " said the major, gesticulating with his lead-pencil as if he would stab him with it.

" And our feelings, which——"

" How much do you earn outside? " The major began to scrawl something on his blotting-paper.

" Oh! that surely will not fail, if we only first——"

" Will you answer me, or not? How much do you earn outside? Figures are what I want—figures and facts."

" I make translations at ten crowns per folio. I give French lessons, too, and some proof-reading is promised me."

" Promises are not facts. Figures, my young man, figures.

So! I am putting it down. How much translating have you to do?"

"How much? Ah! that I cannot say exactly."

"What! you cannot say? Well, then, will you tell me what it is?"

"I am translating Guizot's 'History of Civilization,' twenty-five folios thick, into Swedish."

"Ten crowns each folio makes all together two hundred and fifty crowns. And then——"

"Then—then— That no one can tell beforehand."

"What! one cannot know beforehand? But one should know exactly. You seem to think that marriage is only for passing the time as pleasantly as possible! No, young man; in a year the children begin to come, and children must have food and clothing."

"But the children do not always come so quickly, and when one loves as we love——"

"How the devil do you love, then?"

"How do we love each other?" At this Gustav Falk laid his hand on his heart and rolled up his eyes.

"Do no children come when one loves as you do, you rascal? That is really delicious! However, you are a good enough sort of fellow, and so I give my consent to the betrothal. Make use of your engagement time, though, so that you may earn something, for hard times are facing us. The price of wheat is going up."

Secretary Falk became quite red in the face as he heard this conclusion, yet his joy at obtaining Louisa was so great that he was moved to kiss the old man's hand. God in heaven, how happy he was! And how happy his Louisa! As they walked for the first time in the street arm in arm, every one looked at them. You would suppose that every one halted to form a guard of honor for their triumphal procession. On they swept, with glances uplifted proudly.

In the evening he came to her. They sat down in the middle of the drawing-room and read proof. The old man thought he was a capable fellow; and when the work was done the bridegroom said to the bride, " Now we have earned three crowns ! " A kiss sealed the deed. But on the next evening they went to the theater, and drove home. That cost ten crowns. Sometimes, when he had evening lessons to give—what will one not do for love?—he excused himself from the lessons and went to see his Louisa. Then they went out and took a walk.

The wedding-day drew near; all was changed then. They betook themselves to Brunkeberger Square to choose furniture. They began with the most important. Louisa did not wish to be present when the beds were being bought; but as it turned out she went, all the same. They must be of walnut—each piece of solid walnut. And they must have red-bordered mattresses, with springs, of course, and the pillows filled with eider-down. Each must have its especial eider-down quilt too. Louisa wanted a blue one, because she was blonde. Then they went to the house-furnisher's. First, of course, they chose a red-shaded night-lamp and a bisque Venus; then table service of every variety; fine knives and forks—a couple of dozen; and cut glass, with monogram. At last came the turn for the kitchen dishes, and in that mama must help. Lord! how fearfully busy the bridegroom was ! making out checks, running to the bank, going after workmen, looking up houses, and putting up curtains. He became in arrears with his work. Once he was married, however, he would make all that up. So he thought. They would only rent two rooms to start with. They had resolved to be "reasonable." And if it was only two rooms, they could furnish them so much the more prettily. So he found a dwelling of two rooms, with kitchen and pantry, in the Regierung Strasse, on the first floor, for six hundred crowns. When Louisa let fall the remark that she would just as soon have three rooms and a kitchen on the fourth floor, he grew embarrassed. But what mattered it when one was fond of another? Louisa thought so, too, finally.

The rooms were soon furnished. The bedroom was like a little temple. The beds stood near each other like two chariots in which life's journey was to be made. And the sun shone on the blue coverlid, the snow-white sheets, and the pillows with their monograms embroidered by an old aunt. These were large letters of brier-rose, intertwined as if in embrace, and whenever they met in a knot they kissed each other. A little alcove was arranged for the wife, with a Japanese screen, and in the drawing-room, which was dining-room, study, and reception-room as well, stood her upright piano, which had cost twelve hundred crowns. There also was his writing-desk of old walnut, a large plate-glass mirror, sofa, reading-table, and dining-table. It looked as if people who knew how to lead a comfortable and cozy life lived there.

At last came the wedding. It was on a Saturday evening. Thereupon followed Sunday morning. What a life! Oh, how delightful it is to be married! What a glorious invention marriage is! Then one may do what one pleases.

In the morning, at nine o'clock, the bedroom was still dark. The young groom did not wish to open the shutters yet. He lighted the red lamp again and threw its magical light on the blue coverlid and upon the somewhat rumpled white sheets. The bisque Venus stood saucy and inviting in the rosy glow. There lay the pretty young wife, so delightfully languid, and as happy as if this were the first night of her life in which she had slept well. No wagons were to be heard on the streets, for the day was Sunday, and the bells rang so cheerily, so joyfully, as if they would call all mankind together to give thanks that man and wife were created. He whispered in her ear. She should turn over, so that he could go out and order breakfast. She buried her little head in the pillows, while he went behind the screen in order to put on the absolutely necessary things. He entered the drawing-room, where the sun threw a broad, beaming ray upon the floor. At first, for a moment, he did not know whether it was spring, summer, autumn, or winter. He only knew that it was Sunday. His bachelor days seemed to him like a dark shadow from which he had escaped, and in his new dwelling he breathed the breath of his old home and his future family. Oh, how strong he felt! His future loomed up before him like a tottering hill. He rushed at it; it broke in sand beneath his feet, and he set forward upon his way over chimney and housetop with his pure young bride in his arms.

Then he picked up his clothes, lying scattered on the floor; his white cravat he found perched on a picture-frame, like a butterfly. He went into the kitchen. Oh, how splendidly the new copper utensils glimmered and glistened! And the tin cooking-kettles! All that belonged to him and to her! He called the cook. She received the direction to order a breakfast from the Restaurant of the Three Romans at once. It must be fine. The host already knew; she need only tell him.

He then returned to the bedroom door and knocked. " May I come in? " A little shriek; then, " No, my love; wait just a minute."

163

Now he lays the table himself. When the breakfast came he filled the new plates, folded the napkins beautifully, and wiped the wine-glasses. The bridal bouquet paraded in front of his wife's plate. And now out she comes in her embroidered morning-gown, and the sunbeams meet her. She is a little faint, only a little, so he pushes her in an easy chair up to the table. Quick! a little Kümmel in a liqueur-glass; a bit of bread with caviar. That helps. Oh, how glorious! One may do everything one chooses, if one is but married. Only to think what mama would say if she saw her daughter drinking *Schnaps!* He waits on her; runs and springs as if he still were her betrothed. But the breakfast after such a night! And no one had the right to criticize him! Often enough already had he had such break-fasts. But what a difference! Discontent, restlessness, he puts behind him; and as he drinks a glass of real porter with his oysters he cannot despise bachelors enough. Just to think of the stupid men who do not marry! Such egoists should be taxed, like dogs. The young wife ventured to demur, yet as gently and lovingly as possible, that the poor fellows who do not wish to marry are rather to be pitied. If they could, surely they would, all of them. That gave the secretary a little stab at the heart. He became meditative for a moment. He had been so overflowing with spirits. All his happiness was based on a question of economics. And when—when— Bah! a glass of Burgundy! Work will soon begin. Then we shall see. Next comes the roast pheasant, and with it delicious cranberries and cucumbers.

The young wife, a little concerned about the luxurious meal, laid her trembling hand upon his arm, and said, "Dear heart, can we allow ourselves all this?" Luckily she said "we."

"One day is not every day," he replied. "Herring and potatoes we can eat later, and often enough."

"Do you really eat herring and potatoes?"

"Well, I should think so."

"Yes, when you have been out and come in with a heavy head, and a beefsteak à *la Chateaubriand* follows."

"Do not talk about it. Your health! That was faultless, that pheasant, and such artichokes!"

"No, Gustav; you are quite reckless. Artichokes at this time of year! What will that cost?"

"Are they not good? That is the main point. And now a little glass of wine! More wine! Don't you think life is beautiful? Oh, glorious! glorious!"

Exactly at six o'clock, before the door stood an elegant carriage in livery. The young wife scarcely believed her eyes. And how lovely that was—half lying side by side, and gently rocked, to ride to the park! Acquaintances they met on the way greeted them, and comrades waved their hands and seemed to say, "Ha-ha, you sly dog! You have married money." Oh, how small people looked down below there! And however uneven the road, how easy the ride on the upholstered springs! So it should always be.

It lasted so a whole month—balls, companies, dinners, suppers, theaters. Betweenwhiles they were at home. That was really the best of all. How delightful after the supper to take his wife away from papa and mama; to put her in a closed carriage right before their faces; to nod to the dear parents and bid them good-by; and then to say, "We will go home, and do there just as we please!" At home a little supper followed, and then they sat and talked until morning. At home Gustav was always prudent—that is, in principle. One day the young wife wished to attempt smoked

salmon, boiled potatoes, and oat soup. How good it tasted!
Still Gustav was somewhat out of humor over this menu.
On the next Friday, when it was to be salmon again, he
came home with a brace of partridges. He stood in the
doorway, exclaiming, " Can you imagine anything so unheard-of, Louisa ? "

" Why, what ? "

" You will scarcely believe when I tell you. I bought both
of these partridges at the market. Guess for how much ? "

The young wife was so angry that she scarcely wished to
guess.

" Only think, a crown for the pair ! "

Louisa had once bought a pair of partridges at eighty öre,
but she did not mention it, so as not to hurt her husband's
feelings.

" But, anyhow, you will admit that they are cheap ? "

She must agree, if only to please him. For the evening
there was oatmeal just for a trial. After Gustav had eaten a
partridge, he was sorry not to eat as much oatmeal as he
had really meant to. He would gladly have shown that
the porridge pleased him. He really liked oatmeal, only he
could not endure milk with it. He would eat oatmeal every
evening, if only his wife would not be displeased with him.
After this, of course, there was an end to oatmeal. He never
had it served to him again. Six weeks passed, and the young
wife grew ill. She had headaches and nausea, probably in
consequence of a cold. But the nausea did not stop. Hm!
Had she by any chance poisoned herself? Was it the fault
of the copper kettles? The doctor was called. He laughed,
and said it was all in order. What was in order? Something suspicious! How was that possible? No; it came
from the bedroom paper. There was certainly arsenic in it.

Send it to the chemist at once, and let it be analyzed. " Free
from arsenic," wrote the chemist. That was remarkable—
no arsenic in the wall-paper. The young wife's sickness continued. Gustav studied a medical book, and whispered something in her ear. Yes, that's it; now we have it. Ha-ha!
Only a warm foot-bath. Four weeks afterward the nurse declared that all was safe. Safe—horrible! That is clear. But
it came so quick. Still, now it was settled, and how lovely it
would be! Think, a child! Hurrah! They would be papa
and mama. What should they call it? It would be a boy,
of course; that was certain. But now Louisa took her husband aside and spoke earnestly to him. Since his marriage
he had not busied himself with translating or proof-reading.
His salary alone was not sufficient. "Yes, yes! they had
lived in riot and revel." Lord! one is never young but once.
However, now all should be different."

On the next day the secretary went to his old friend the
notary and begged him to go security for a loan. "When
one is about to become a father, my dear sir, one must think
of the increase in expenses."

"I agree with you perfectly," answered the notary; " on
that account I have never ventured to marry. You are indeed a lucky fellow. You were able to do so."

The secretary was ashamed to press his request. How
could he have the face to ask this bachelor, who had not
ventured to marry on account of his small income, for a
loan for himself and his child? No, that he could not do.

When he came home in the evening his wife told him two
men had been there looking for him. "How did they look?
Were they young? Did they wear eye-glasses? They surely
were two lieutenants, good old friends from Vaxholm."

"They were not lieutenants. They looked much older."

"Indeed!" Now he knew. They were old friends from Upsala. Probably Dr. P. and Deputy O., who wished to see how the old fellow bore married life.

"No, they were not from Upsala. They were Stockholmers."

The maid was called. She thought they looked suspicious, and they had sticks.

"Sticks! Hm! Who could that be? We shall soon learn when they come again."

In the meantime he had been to the market, and had bought a can of strawberries at a bargain—at a really absurd price. "Only think, a can of pineapple strawberries for a crown and a half, now, at this time of year!"

"Gustav! Gustav! What is going to become of us?"

"Don't be anxious. I have arranged for a new piece of work to-day."

"But the debts, Gustav?"

"Trifles! Only wait till I secure a large loan."

"A loan? Then that will be a new debt."

"Yes, but at what terms! Let us not talk of such things. Were not the strawberries good? What? Would not a little glass of sherry go well afterward? What do you say? Lina, go to the wine-dealer for a bottle of sherry—genuine, mind."

After the midday nap on the sofa his wife begged to be allowed to say two words, but he must not be angry. Angry! He? God forbid! Probably money for the house.

"Well, then. The grocer is not paid. The butcher gives us warning. The liveryman wants his money. All that is, in a word, extremely disagreeable."

"Nothing more? They shall have their money, every crown, to-morrow morning. What impudence to give warning for such trifles! But to-morrow they shall be paid everything. Moreover, they will lose a customer. But now we will talk no more of that. We will take a little walk. No carriage? We will go in the tram to the park to get a little fresh air."

So they rode to the park, and took a private room in the Alhambra. The young men in the dining-room whispered. They thought it was a pair out for a lark. So jolly, so exciting! But the wife did not quite like it. And then the bill. What could they not have had at home for that money?

Months pass. The time draws near. A cradle is needed —underclothing and dresses for the little one, and so much of everything. The secretary is busy all day. The price of grain had really risen. Hard times were at hand. No translations, no proof-reading. The world had grown so material. They do not buy books any more. They use their money for bread. In what prosaic times we live! The ideal vanishes. Partridges cannot be bought under two crowns a pair. The liveryman will not drive for nothing any more, for he also has a wife and children; and even the grocer wants money for his goods. Oh, what realists! At last the eventful day arrives. The moment is near. He must run and fetch the nurse. From the sick-bed he must go out into the hall to receive his creditors. He carries his daughter in his arms. Tears come to his eyes. He feels the responsibilities weighing upon him more heavily than his strength can bear, and he makes new resolutions. But his nerves are upset. He had secured a translation, but he could not stick to it, for he had to go out continually on errands.

He rushed with the joyful tidings to his father-in-law, who had come into the city. "I am a father!"

"Good! Have you bread, too, for your child?"

"At present, no. Father-in-law must help."

"This time, yes; this time, but never again in the future. I have little more than you, and, besides, the other children must have something."

The invalid must have chicken to eat now, which he himself buys at the market, and genuine Johannisberger at six crowns a bottle. The nurse receives a hundred crowns. Why should they give less than others do? The captain gave a hundred crowns too. The young wife is soon on her feet again. Like a young girl once more, slender as a willow, a little pale; but that is becoming to her. The father-in-law comes and takes Gustav aside. "Now be so good as not to come to me for a while with any more children," said he, "or otherwise you will be ruined."

"What a speech for a father! Are we not man and wife? Do we not love each other, and are we not to have children?"

"Yes, but also bread for your children. All young people love easily. But the responsibility!"

The father-in-law is a materialist too. Wretched times without any ideality!

The life of the house was undermined; but love did not allow itself to be repressed, for it was strong, and young intentions are weak. But creditors are not weak. Bankruptcy threatened. An attachment was imminent. The father-in-law came with a large wagon and carried off his daughter and grandchild. He forbade the son-in-law to show himself until he had bread for them, and had paid his debts. To his daughter he said nothing. But as he rode away it seemed to him as if he had brought home a ruined maiden. He had lent out his pure child to a young man for a year, and now he had received her back again. Louisa would gladly have remained with her husband, but she could not live with her child upon the street. So Gustav must remain behind, and look on while his home was made desolate. Even that did not belong to him, for it was not paid for. The two men with the eye-glasses took beds, copper and pewter, china, chandeliers—everything, everything. And as he stood there alone in the empty room, how disheartening it was for him! If she had only stayed! But what could she do in those empty rooms? It was better so.

The bitter earnest of life began. He obtained a position on a morning paper as proof-reader. He had to be at the office at midnight, and stay there three hours. He retained his official position, because he had not yet come to bankruptcy, but he was cut off from advancement. At last he was granted permission to see his wife and daughter once a week, but even then not in private. At night he slept in a little room near his father-in-law's. Sunday evening he had to go back to the city, for the paper was published early on Monday morning. Then he took leave of wife and child, who accompanied him to the garden-gate, and he waved to them from afar, and felt so unhappy, so miserable, so humiliated. And she?

He had reckoned that it would take him twenty years to pay his debts. After that? After that he would still be unable to provide for wife and child. Upon what, then, was any hope to be based? On nothing. If his father-in-law should die, wife and child would have nothing at all. He did not venture, therefore, to curse his only prop.

Oh, how pitiless is life! It provides no sustenance for the children of men, while it gives food to all other created beings. And that this life does not offer all men partridges and strawberries—really, it is too hard!

Karl Hedenstjerna

Aunt Louise's Mirror

THE Strömbom couple lived happy and contented; not so happy and contented, to be sure, as during the time of their engagement, for they had discovered that he smoked one hundred and fifty crowns' worth of cigars during the year, and that she had an old aunt who needed a monthly allowance of ten crowns. Nevertheless, she did not feel the least desire to throttle him when he lay snoring in bed a long while after she had arisen, and he had never felt an inner necessity for throwing the poker after her when she left the room with the remark that the new curtains were full of smoke again. And so it seems to me that, as things go in this world, the marriage could be called a happy one. Their income sufficed for furniture stuffed with straw. In short, they were simple people, who had their fill of food thrice a day, but not of a delicacy to tempt them to overeating.

They had two children, who were not more unkempt than other children of the same age. But if visitors came, papa would receive them at the door of the drawing-room, mama would capture the children, and for a quarter of an hour one would hear from afar the splashing of water, the crisp noise of bitten thread—the scissors being momentarily mislaid—sharp taps on childish cheeks, and little cries, " Oh, how cross you are, mama! " And then the little Strömboms would come in with moist hair and a penetrating odor of cheap soap. But God had not so ordered it that this happy

172

condition of the family should last, for, in His mercy, He sent Aunt Louise on a visit to the Strömboms.

Aunt Louise was a gruff, tough old woman of seventy, and the only chance of her leaving the world rested on the hope that her nose and chin, which had gradually been approaching each other for many years, would finally grow together and so stop her breathing. As yet, however, half an inch was lacking.

For seven weeks she sweetened the life of the Strömbom family, and then decided to make them a handsome present before her departure. And so toward the end of the seventh week she went to a large auction sale, and there she bought an elegant mirror, that had originally cost four hundred and fifty crowns, for forty-seven crowns and sixty öre, and had it brought to the Strömboms' house. On the next day she departed.

Until now the family had had only one maid of all work. Mrs. Strömbom attended to the children herself; that is to say, she permitted them to develop a healthy independence, interfering only when they had swallowed too many pins, come to grief by rolling heavy articles of furniture over each other, stuck knives or scissors into their eyes, or instituted ink wells in the carpet. But on the day on which Aunt Louise's mirror arrived, mama saw her little Charles stand before it and measure it. She took him by the arm, called him her dear naughty boy, and declared to papa Strömbom that she would have to have a nurse. It would not cost much to have one, and would, at all events, come cheaper than if the children broke Aunt Louise's mirror. The nurse came, but a few days thereafter Mrs. Strömbom was attacked by a fearful headache, tore open her dress, threw herself on the sofa, and seemed in danger of instant dissolution. By patient and tender solicitude, her husband finally elicited the information that the seat of her suffering lay in the old carpet of the drawing-room, so completely at variance with the splendid mirror, which should reflect only the delicate pattern of a Brussels carpet. Strömbom sighed, took two hundred and seventy-five crowns from the children's bank-books, and soon an imitation Brussels carpet honored the presence of the mirror.

"Heavenly, my dear friend!" said Mrs. Mealymouth on the following day to Natalie Strömbom. "Your little drawing-room is charming, positively elegant. It would be quite exquisite if you had one of those modern chandeliers with glass prisms that would reflect their many-colored lights in the mirror."

A week later, just such a chandelier—bought on credit—adorned the Strömboms' drawing-room.

Strömbom himself had a sense for the beautiful. He had studied esthetics once, and every time he entered his drawing-room he frowned and sighed.

"What is wrong with you?" asked his spouse; "you sigh like a cow with indigestion."

"My dear, do you not see how entirely out of place our old furniture is with Aunt Louise's mirror and the carpet?"

And so the old sofa—on which Natalie, before her marriage, had enjoyed the dreams and enthusiasms of her virginal youth; on which her father had sat drinking his beer the day before he died; on which Strömbom had proposed to her—this venerable old sofa, with its accompanying chairs, was now sent away. Money was borrowed at a high rate of interest, and a set of mahogany furniture bought. In consequence, the Strömboms starved themselves. Only he was permitted now and then to take a meal at a restaurant, for fear that his digestive organs might become atrophied through disuse. But Aunt Louise's mirror had the satisfaction of reflecting surroundings worthy of its own splendor.

Need I relate how new loans were made in order to make the other rooms harmonize with the drawing-room? Need I relate how they lied and borrowed in order to be able to entertain liberally? For what is the use of the most elegant house if no one comes to see it?

And so every one believed that Strömbom had grown rich. The assessor of taxes doubled Strömbom's rating. The clergyman came and asked for twenty-five crowns for the establishment of schools of domestic science for the growing daughters of the cannibals. The cook asked for higher wages on account of the many dinners that were given. The rich and childless Uncle John wrote, " Since I have noticed with great pleasure that you have worked yourself up to so excellent a position, and that your home is now one of the most elegant in the city, I have changed my will, and have left my money as a pension fund for deserving female servants."

And so Strömbom went into bankruptcy, and all the splendors were sold at auction, Aunt Louise's mirror bringing seventy-five crowns.

Strömbom went to the young clergyman who had bought the mirror, and said, " My dear sir, have a care of that mirror. It brings ill luck."

The young clergyman turned up his eyes, closed them, then folded his hands, and said, " All things work together for good to them that love God."

There was a great gossiping-party at Aunt Louise's when the letter came announcing Strömbom's bankruptcy. She clasped her hands in horror, and exclaimed, " There, you see what happens when people do not know how to manage! And all their relatives tried to help them! I myself gave them a magnificent mirror."—"*Stories and Sketches.*"

Rural Travelers

THE train going south left the station at a quarter past twelve, but by eight o'clock the travelers had already reached the station. After many exhortations to the stableman to ᴅᴇ careful of the sorrel, and a dozen commands to the maid-servant, seven persons approached the station hand in hand —four hours too soon—to buy tickets. At that time the traffic at the smaller stations was quite inconsiderable; only a few trains passed during the day, so that none of the officials thought it necessary to be at the station so early.

But farmer Strömbom had no intention of waiting, and went off to the station-master's house to " come to an agreement," as he put it, concerning the amount of the fare.

" Good morning," he said to that official. " My name is Strömbom—Peter Strömbom of Traleböda, of which you will have heard. I am minded to travel with my wife and children to Malmö, to visit my brother, the merchant Johann Strömbom, of whom you will also have heard."

Strömbom's method did not arouse the surprise in those early days of the Swedish railroads that it would to-day. The officials were accustomed to that kind of thing. Hence the station-master said, " Very well, you will find the 12.15 train convenient."

" All right. But then, I wanted to discuss the question of

fares with you. I am told that you charge seven crowns for the trip to Malmö."

" Seven crowns and fifteen öre."

" Pooh, pooh! The fifteen öre are there, I suppose, so that you can make a reduction. So let's stick to the seven crowns. Now, there are seven of us, my wife and five children, so I suppose it will come cheaper for all."

" Probably, since children under twelve pay only half fare."

" I know that, but I mean a reduction on the whole."

" That is impossible, my dear sir, for the State demands from us the whole amount of the prescribed fare."

" Hm—you don't take an extra coach on our account."

" Certainly not, but——"

" You see, I can easily send the two youngest children back home."

" That is your business."

" And so the State must lose those two fares through your obstinacy? "

" The fare is fixed by law. You may travel or not, as you please."

" Oh! very well, then. But at least there must be no mistake about the train stopping for half an hour between Hestveda and Hassleholm, so that I can run over to the place of my friend Ole Holm."

" The train stops nowhere except at the stations printed on the time-table."

" You will permit me to remark," cried Strömbom, " that you are the most disobliging person it has ever been my misfortune to meet! "—" *Brothers and Sisters.*"

Dutch Wit and Humor

Erasmus of Rotterdam

A Young Man and an Echo

Young Man. I have a mind to ask your advice about a few things, if you are at leisure——

Echo. I am at leisure——

Young Man. And if I, a young man, shall be welcome to you.

Echo. You are welcome.

Young Man. Can you tell me true concerning things to come?

Echo. I can.

Young Man. Do you understand Greek too?

Echo. I do.

Young Man. What do you consider studies of the Muses to be?

Echo. Divine studies.

Young Man. Do you think, then, that the authors that conduce to learning ought to be studied?

Echo. Them you should study.

Young Man. But what is in the minds of those who speak contemptuously of such studies?

Echo. The thoughts of swine.

Young Man. Yet I wish the lovers of these studies were as fond of piety.

Echo. So do I.

Young Man. Nowadays, the wickedness of some draws hatred upon many.

Echo. It does, on many.

Erasmus of Rotterdam

Young Man. And many lay the sins of man on the back of learning.

Echo. Yes, asses.

Young Man. But they commonly seem not to be of the meanest sort.

Echo. They are vile persons.

Young Man. Do you not think that those who spend their time upon a sophistical kind of learning spin cobwebs?

Echo. They do.

Young Man. And do they not weave and unweave Penelope's web?

Echo. They do weave it.

Young Man. What course of life do you advise me to follow?

Echo. A safe one.

Young Man. Will it prove fortunate if I should marry?

Echo. Do it late.

Young Man. But what if it should happen to be my lot to marry an unchaste or extravagant wife?

Echo. You must bear it.

Young Man. Why, but it is worse than death to live with such!

Echo. It is so.

Young Man. Does Fortune thus govern human affairs?

Echo. Yes, she only.

Young Man. Perhaps, rather than marry, one should become a monk?

Echo. That also binds one.

Young Man. Then, what remedy is left, when one is tied by a knot which cannot be unloosed?

Echo. Melancholy.

Dutch Wit and Humor

Young Man. Well, but it is a miserable sort of life for men to live alone.

Echo. It is entirely so.

Young Man. What sort of men do you account the monks of these times to be?

Echo. Troublesome.

Young Man. What, then, makes some esteem them as half-gods?

Echo. Fear.

Young Man. What do they most seek who sue for a benefice?

Echo. Idleness.

Young Man. Does a priest get nothing else?

Echo. Yes, gain.

Young Man. What good thing do they get who obtain bishoprics?

Echo. Labor.

Young Man. But none live in greater idleness.

Echo. I know it.

Young Man. What things will be able to make them think, and understand what a great burden they have upon them?

Echo. Understanding.

Young Man. Therefore, the priesthood is a desirable life, if a man behave himself as he ought in it?

Echo. It makes him happy.

Young Man. What advantage shall I have if I go into their court who excel in princely dignity?

Echo. Misery.

Young Man. But I see a great many that are wont to promise themselves much happiness therefrom.

Echo. They are blockheads.

Young Man. But in the meantime, while they go clothed

in their silks, the common people look upon them as **fine** fellows.

Echo. They are not worth a fig.

Young Man. Why, then, those men who are arrayed in silk, and whom we worship almost as gods, have not much excellency within them?

Echo. They have mischief.

Young Man. And perhaps you put no great value upon military men?

Echo. A farthing.

Young Man. The astrologers, however, who tell fortunes by the stars, are able to promise great things.

Echo. Fables.

Young Man. As to grammarians, then: they are men who take great pains.

Echo. To no purpose.

Young Man. Neither do hungry, greedy lawyers please you, I suppose?

Echo. They are wolves.

Young Man. What sort of man shall I be if I pursue a handicraft?

Echo. The scum of the people.

Young Man. Why, then, do neither good occupations nor bad procure one anything desirable?

Echo. A maintenance.

Young Man. Shall I be happy if I persevere in profound study?

Echo. You will.

Young Man. But what will make me pious?

Echo. Age.

Young Man. I have spent my time these ten years on Cicero.

Dutch Wit and Humor

Echo. You are an ass.

Young Man. How comes it that you call me an ass?

Echo. Because of the thing itself.

Young Man. Perhaps you mean I should not devote so much application to him as to make me neglect others?

Echo. I do say so.

Young Man. Then, does not he please you who fatigues himself all his days only for the one purpose that he may become a Ciceronian at last?

Echo. He is a madman.

Young Man. What is left for them to do who are old, whose age is not seasonable for the learning of these things?

Echo. The plow-tail.

Young Man. I believe you would be more eloquent if you were at a greater distance.

Echo. I should be so.

Young Man. I don't like words of two syllables.

Echo. Go your way.

Young Man. I began first, and I see I can't hinder your having the last word.

Echo. Let me have it.

Young Man. Do you now think I am sufficiently instructed to perform those things well which shall happen in life?

Echo. Yes.

Young Man. Well, then, if you would have me go away, bid me begone.

Echo. Begone.—" *Colloquies.*"

Jacob Cats

Cupid Lost

THE child of Venus, wanton, wild,
The sliest rogue that ever smiled,
Has lately strayed—where, who shall guess?
His mother pines in sad distress;
She calls the boy, she sighs, complains,
But still no news of Cupid gains;
For, though her sorrow grows apace,
None knows the urchin's resting-place.
She therefore vows the boy shall be
Cried o'er the country publicly:

" If there be any who can tell
Where little Cupid now doth dwell,
A fit reward he shall enjoy
If he track out the truant boy;
His recompense a fragrant kiss
From Venus's ruby mouth of bliss.
But he who firmly holds the knave
Shall yet a sweeter guerdon have.
Now, lest ye should mistake the wight,
List to his form described aright:
He is a little wayward thing
That's panoplied on fiery wing;
Two pinions, like a swan, he carries,
And never for an instant tarries,

Dutch Wit and Humor

But now is here, and now is there,
And couples many a curious pair.
His eyes like two bright stars are glowing,
And ever sidelong glances throwing.
He bears about a crafty bow,
And wounds before the wounded know;
His dart, though gilt to please the view,
Is dipped in bitter venom too.
His body, though 'tis bare to sight,
Has overthrown full many a knight;
His living torch, though mean and small,
Oft makes the hardiest warrior fall,
The highest dames with care invades,
And spares not e'en the tenderest maids.
Nay, what is worse than all the rest,
He sometimes wounds his mother's breast.

" If such an urchin should be found,
Proclaim the joyous news around;
And should the boy attempt to fly,
Then seize him right courageously.
But if you have the child at last,
Be careful that you hold him fast,
Or else th' elusive bird he'll play,
And vanish in thin air away.
Yet, if he seem to pine and grieve,
You must not heed him, nor believe,
Nor trust his tears and feigned distress,
His winning glance and bland caress;
But watch his cheek when dimples wreathe it,
And think that evil lurks beneath it;

Jacob Cats

For under his pretended smile
Are veiled the deepest craft and guile.
If he a kiss should offer, shun
The proffered gift, or be undone;
His pretty lips thy heart would sentence
To brief delight, but long repentance.
But if the cunning boy would give
His dart to you, oh, ne'er receive,
If you would hope for blissful years,
The present that so fair appears:
It is no pledge of love, but shame,
And danger, and destroying flame.

" Then, friends, to speak with brevity,
This wholesome warning take from me:
Let those who seize the wily ranger
Be on their guard 'gainst every danger;
For, if they venture too securely,
Misfortunes will assail them surely;
And, if they trust the boy in aught,
The catchers will themselves be caught."

E. D. Dekker—" Multatuli "

Droogstoppel's Views on Education

I AM a coffee-broker, and live at No. 37 Lauriergracht. It is not my custom to write novels, or any such thing; so it was a long time before I made up my mind to order a couple of reams of paper and begin the work which you, dear reader, have just taken up, and which you ought to read if you are in the coffee business—or, in fact, if you are anything else. And not only have I never written anything which was in the least like a novel, but I don't hold with even reading anything of the sort, because I am a man of business. For several years past I have been asking myself, What is the use of such things? And I am perfectly amazed at the impudence of poets and novelists in palming off upon you things which have never happened, and, for the most part, never can happen. Now, in *my* business—I am a coffee-broker, and live in the Lauriergracht, No. 37—if I were to send in to a principal (a principal is a man who sells coffee) an account containing only a small part of the untruths which are the main point in all poems and romances, why, he would at once go to Busselinck & Waterman. (Busselinck & Waterman are coffee-brokers too; but it is not necessary for you to know *their* address.) So I take good care not to write any novels or send in wrong accounts. I have always noticed that persons who let themselves in for that kind of thing generally get the worst of it. I am forty-three, and have been at the Exchange for twenty years, so that I have every right to put myself forward when a man of experience

E. D. Dekker

is in demand. I have seen plenty of firms fail in my time; and usually, when I examined into the causes of their failure, it seemed to me that they must be sought for in the wrong direction given to most people in their youth.

I say, "Truth and sound sense!" And that I stick to. The mistake comes in, in the first place, with Van Alphen, even in his very first line about the "dear little creatures." What on earth could induce this old gentleman to call himself an adorer of my little sister Triutje, who had sore eyes, or of my brother Gerrit, who was always biting his nails? And yet he says that "he sang these verses, compelled by love." I used often to think, when I was a child, "Man, I *should* like to meet you, just for once; and then, if you refused me the marbles I should ask you for, or the whole of my name in chocolate letters, then I should consider you a liar." But I never saw Van Alphen. I think he was already dead when he used to tell us that my father was my best friend—I thought far more of Pauweltje Winser, who lived next door to us—and that my little dog was so grateful for kindness! We never kept dogs, because they are dirty.

That is the way children are brought up; and, later on, come other lies again. A girl is an angel! The man who was the first to discover that never had any sisters of his own. Love is bliss! One is going to fly, with one object or another, to the end of the earth. The earth has no ends; and, besides, love is madness. No one can say that I do not live happily with my wife. She is a daughter of Last & Co., coffee-brokers. I am a member of the most respectable club in Amsterdam. She has a shawl that cost ninety-two florins. And yet there was never any question between us of a foolish love like that, which insists on living at the very

187

end of the earth! When we were married we made a little tour to The Hague; she bought some flannel there, and I am wearing undervests made of it to this day; but love never drove us out into the world any farther than that. Bah! it is all madness and lies!

It is not verses alone that seduce the young into untruthfulness. Just go to the theater and listen to the falsehoods that are being spread abroad there. The hero of the play is pulled out of the water by some fellow on the point of going into the bankruptcy court. Then he gives the fellow half his fortune. Why, such a thing could not possibly happen! Not long ago, when my hat was blown into the Prinsengracht, I gave the man who brought it back to me four cents, and he was quite satisfied. Of course I know I should have had to give something more if it had been myself that he pulled out, but certainly not half what I possess. Why, it is quite clear that, on this principle, one need only fall into the water twice to be ruined! But the worst of it is, with such things represented on the stage, the public gets so accustomed to all these falsehoods that it thinks them fine, and applauds them. I should just like to throw a whole pitful of such people into the water, and see whose applause was sincere. I, who hold by the truth, warn every one that I am not going to pay so high a salvage for the fishing up of my person. Any one who is not satisfied with less may just let me stay where I am. On a Sunday, however, I should pay rather more, because then I wear my gold watchchain and my best coat.

Yes, the stage ruins many—still more than the novels. It looks so well! With a little gold tinsel and paper lace things can be made so attractive—for children, that is to say, and for people who are not in business. Even when

E. D. Dekker

they want to represent poverty on the stage, the picture given is always a false one. A girl, whose father has gone bankrupt, is working to keep the family. Very good. There she sits, then, sewing, knitting, or embroidering. But just count the stitches that she takes in the course of the whole scene. She talks, she sighs, she keeps running to the window, but she does not work. The family who can live on such work as this must have few wants indeed. Of course a girl like this is the heroine. She has thrown several villains down the stairs. She continually calls out, " Oh, mother ! mother ! " and thus represents virtue. What sort of virtue do you call that, that takes a year to finish a pair of woolen socks ? Does not all this give people wrong ideas about virtue and working for their living?

Then her first lover—he was formerly a clerk at the copying-book, but now a millionaire—suddenly comes back and marries her. Lies again. A man with money will never marry a girl from a house that has failed. And then, virtue rewarded! I have had plenty of experience in my time, but still it shocks me terribly when I see truth perverted in this way. Virtue rewarded! Isn't it just like making a traffic out of virtue? It is not so in this world, and a very good thing it is that it is not. Where is the merit of being virtuous, if virtue is to be rewarded? Now, I am as virtuous as most people, but do I expect to be rewarded for it? If my business goes on well—which, in fact, it does; if my wife and children keep in health, so that I have no worry with the doctor and chemist; if, year by year, I can put away a little sum for my old age; if Fritz grows up a good man of business, so that he can step into my shoes when I retire and go to live at Driebergen—well, if all these things are so, I am quite content. But all that is a natural result of circumstances, and of my attention to business. I don't ask any special reward for my virtue.

That I am virtuous is quite evident from my love for truth. This, next to my attachment to our orthodox belief, is my ruling passion. And I should like the reader to be quite convinced of this, because it is my excuse for writing this book.—" *Max Havelaar.*"

Arnold Buning

Romance on Shipboard

SEATED on a tub turned upside down, close to the foremast, Jozef is reading aloud by the light of a lantern out of an "awfully fine" book.

The boy can read "first-rate"; and from each of the listeners seated round him he is to receive the sum of two cents.

The book which he now has before him, and which is covered with oil-stains, because he has to hold it so close to the lantern—the book which is so "awfully fine" is entitled "Count Matatskai; or, The Bandit with the Gray Beard: A Story of the Mountains."

Count Matatskai is a youthful nobleman who has fallen in love with a mountain maiden, the beautiful but fierce Krimhelia, daughter of a chamois-hunter. After various meetings on the rocks by moonlight, with a faithful old servitor *incognito* in the background, Krimhelia makes up her mind to accept the count's love, and fly with him to a distant country, where counts and the daughters of chamois-hunters stand precisely on the same social footing. But now a difficulty occurs, and it is this: Krimhelia has sworn an oath to avenge the death of her father, who has been killed in a fight with the band commanded by the gray-bearded brigand.

This is the point Jozef has reached in the story. Several of his audience have already dropped asleep, but the reader does not notice it; he is too much absorbed in his narrative, and continues in his "first-rate" manner, which, heard at a distance, reminds one of nothing so much as of the soft but continuous murmur of a babbling brook—commas and other stops being, in this method, so entirely left in the background, or else occurring in such remarkable places, that a reporter would have been forced to reproduce his text somewhat as follows:

" Krimhelia looked the count straight in the face.

" ' Look at me count' said she ' do you see this glittering dagger as sure as the moon, hangs yonder in heaven and illuminates my pale features so surely will I thrust this, dagger into the heart of the bandit, with the gray beard first and before I throw myself as your consort into your arms but why so pale count and why do you tremble so? ' "

Here Jozef is interrupted by the master tailor, a thin little man, of whom it is commonly said on board that he knows a thing or two more than most people.

" Now, I know—" says he, in his piping voice.

" What d'ye know? " asks the boatswain, who has little or no opinion of the master tailor.

" As how the gentleman—the count, I mean—and the other —the bandit with the gray beard—that both of them are one and the same man."

" Well, you calico-spoiler, you know that, do you? Well, I know that, too, and all of us know it right enough; but you needn't take another man's share in the reading, for all that. —Go ahead, boy! "

The master tailor is looked at with contempt from various quarters, and Jozef pursues his reading with a chapter describing how Count Matatskai comes home in a bad temper:

" The count threw himself down on a, couch adorned with costly velvet, ' relieve me of my riding-boots '—thus he spoke to the gray-headed old servant Gabario who, brought him a

Arnold Buning

silver goblet with sparkling wine saying, that this was his favorite wine from the great vineyard south of the castle but, the count made a gesture of refusal with his left hand and said 'me liketh no wine Gabario avaunt and saddle— my horse!'"

This was the end of the chapter, and Jozef took breath.

"It's a capital thing," said the boatswain, "when a man can have the things for the ordering in that way. What comes next, Jozef?"

The boatswain is beginning to feel sleepy, and would therefore like Jozef to tell him the end at once; but this Jozef is by no means inclined to do; so he goes ahead valiantly, and by degrees, though he does not observe it, his whole audience drops asleep. At last, when he has reached the closing scene, there is no one to listen to it but the master tailor, who can scarcely keep his small gray eyes open.

"Just hear this, now!" says Jozef, who, though he has read the book through twice before, is as enthusiastic over this passage as at the first perusal. "Now you must listen! Now the count is sitting up alone in the rocks, in a cavern, they call it, and now he is the bandit with the gray beard; and the other robbers are sitting in the back of the cavern round a great big fire, and some of them are lying asleep, and the others are roasting great pieces of meat at the fire, and they're drinking wine with it out of gold cups that they've stolen. But the bandit with the gray beard, *he's* sitting all by himself, you see; and now Krimhelia comes in —you know, the young lady he thinks so much of."

And Jozef resumes his reading: how Krimhelia approaches cautiously, with the glittering dagger; how the gray-bearded bandit, looking up, suddenly sees her stand-

193

ing behind him; how Krimhelia seizes him by the beard and drives the dagger into his heart; and how, at the same moment, the long gray beard comes off in her hand, and she looks with horror on the "pallid, dying countenance" of Count Matatskai.

Now follows a dialogue between the dying bandit chief and the "almost fainting" Krimhelia, who is "filled with consternation," in the course of which the tailor finally closes his eyes unobserved.

Now comes the closing scene. The other robbers emerge from behind the fire; Krimhelia takes to flight, and climbs to the top of a steep dark rock on the edge of a "yawning abyss."

As Jozef reads, he bends over his book, leans his head on his hands, and sees the whole thing taking place before his eyes. He sees Krimhelia standing on the top of the rock. The day is breaking in the east. The robbers are pursuing her, and begin to climb the rock.

Jozef reads on, at a passionately accelerated pace, and with the most singular stops imaginable:

"There she stood proudly—like a queen with her long, loose hair and her shining white face standing out sharply against the red sunrise-tinted sky with horror—she saw in the unfathomable depth at her feet the bandits approaching. Already the foremost was stretching out his hand to seize her and she saw, the morning light falling on his horrible features when suddenly, her ear was struck by a sound of men's voices singing beneath her in the valley she listens, it is the morning song of her brothers, she lifts her hands skyward and looks up to the paling moon and the stars 'Iccome!' she cries" (all in one word) "and with a HOARSE shriek she flings herself down into the abyss at the same moment the bandit chief drew his last breath and the Count Matatskai was no more THE END."

"That's all," said Jozef. "That's fine, ain't it? Oh, Lord! They're all asleep!"—"*Naval Sketches.*"

Justus van Maurik

The Commercial Traveler

" Oh, I beg a thousand pardons ! It is indeed stupid of me to come in unannounced, but——"

We were sitting over our breakfast, when a short, hurried knock sounded at the door. I called out, " Come in ! " and saw before me an entire stranger, who, with an embarrassed smile, said the words set down above.

I went to meet him, and said courteously, " Perhaps you are mistaken in the number, or do you really wish to see me ? "

" I beg a thousand pardons ! " he repeated, stepped back a little, and added, " The servant showed me in. I asked whether the master was at home, and she gave me to understand that I would find you in the drawing-room. But I know now how the mistake arose. You have only moved in here recently, have you not ? "

" Only two weeks ago."

" Aha, I thought so. You will permit me to explain myself. Before you, Mr. Zyrok, an intimate friend of mine, lived here ; and so, whenever I passed through town, I was accustomed to call on him, and to walk straight in. I dare say you were surprised."

" Well, yes, I was. But the mistake is a perfectly natural one. Your friend Zyrok has moved to the Heerengracht."

" Ah, indeed ? He told me nothing about it. But forgive me for having disturbed you. Heerengracht, you said ? "

" Yes."

Justus van Maurik

" I'll go there at once. He probably expects me, because his Pontac must be nearly used up."

" I beg your pardon ? " I thought I had not understood.

" His Pontac, I said—vintage of '78. He can't have much left. But, to be sure, I have forgotten to introduce myself. I am the representative of the wine-merchants, Kolik & Co., of The Hague. For years I have furnished my friend with the most excellent wines, and so you understand——"

Oh, yes! I began to understand. Here was a sly fellow indeed, one who knew how to utilize every opportunity.

It occurred to me now that the very day before this I had had a large sign with my name on it fastened to my door. I approached the door, and said, somewhat curtly, " To err is human——"

" To be sure, and therefore you will forgive me. But since chance has brought me into your house, you will permit me to recommend my firm to you. Perhaps you need some fine old Pontac or Larose——"

" I am very sorry—I am supplied with everything."

He did not permit me to finish, but went on with an engaging smile :

" I do not for a moment question the excellence of your cellar, but I should merely like to venture the remark that our Batailly Pontac is a very different thing from the Pontac ordinarily furnished by wine-merchants. The initiated can tell the difference ! "

" Allow me to inform you that, on account of my health, I very seldom drink wine."

" Indeed ? That is very strange. To-day most physicians are of the opinion that a good glass of red wine is excellent —especially our Pontac—even surpassed, perhaps, by our

197

Dutch Wit and Humor

Pomys Agassæ, vintage of '84. Such a *bouquet!* And it is recommended by all physicians——"

"Possibly; but since I suffer from rheumatism, I drink——"

"Little or no wine. And you make a mistake, a very great mistake. Rheumatism is a disease that originates in the blood, and nothing cleanses the blood so thoroughly as a glass of our old red wine. Forty-five bottles for forty-eight florins—delivered at your house. But if you were thinking of buying a cheap table wine, I could recommend our Baour Lénéjac with a good conscience; it is pure and strong, yet light. It is quite absurdly cheap—only thirty-seven florins a keg. My friend Zyrok is crazy over it, and I had to promise to keep a supply of it for him. But since you, on account of your health, are in absolute need of something pure and unadulterated, I would let you have a small keg—only as a sample, of course."

"It is very good of you, but I really cannot make use of your offer."

I approached the door in the hope of getting rid of the philanthropic gentleman. But my hope was short-lived.

"For your own sake I wish you had taken the Baour, but perhaps our Beaujolais would be more to your taste. Do you know Beaujolais?"

"No!"

I began to grow impatient. I put my hand on the knob of the door, and said, "My time is limited, and I must beg you——"

"I understand thoroughly, nor do I wish to detain you. Only I wish to call your attention to the fact that we alone keep this Beaujolais. It has a *bouquet,* an aroma—you cannot imagine it. Something like Burgundy, but lighter. May

198

Justus van Maurik

I send you a sample? I do not wish to persuade you to take a barrel. Heaven forbid! Our firm is far too famous to be obliged to praise its wares. But this Beaujolais is so excellent that I should like to have had your judgment on it. But let me send you a small assortment: one dozen bottles Baour, one dozen Pontac, one dozen Lénéjac, and one Pomys. Then you will see for yourself how excellent our wines are. The head of our firm has vineyards near Kreuznach, so if you need Rhine wine you may get it at its very source."

"You are certainly invaluable!" I exclaimed.

"What do you mean?" he asked courteously.

"Invaluable to your firm. I have never seen such perseverance."

"That is my trade," he said dryly. "But how about port wine? We have a splendid brand—white port. No other firm in Holland has it."

"Thank you, I don't need any port."

"Madeira, perhaps?"

"Nor that either."

"Sherry?"

"No."

"Malaga?"

"Nothing!"

"Marsala des Princes? Or a magnificent Tokay?"

"Sir, I have no more time to waste with you!"

I glanced at the half-open door.

"Yes, you are right. It would be discourteous to keep you any longer, but it would be equally unpardonable if I failed to call your attention to our white Bordeaux: Graves, Haut Sauternes, Château Yquem, Muscatel——"

I was growing more and more impatient. I would never

get rid of the man by normal methods. Then I had a sudden inspiration. Slowly I closed the door.

" Do you happen to know a Mr. Johannes Gram at The Hague? " I said.

" To be sure! How should I fail to know the author of so many excellent stories and sketches? By the way, he is a *connoisseur*. He knows a good glass of wine! "

" Is he a customer of yours? "

" Naturally."

" I thought so."

" Why? "

" I'll tell you. Do you know Mr. Schootmanns? "

" Schootmanns? "

" Yes, the well-known Schootmanns? "

" Oh, him? Of course. A capital fellow. I thought you said Schottmann. But the well-known Schootmanns —he drinks Burgundy—Graves. Would you like to try that? "

" Well—so I was right when I said that in his comedy, *The Well-known Schootmanns,* Graves must have drawn his characters from real life."

" What! a comedy? "

" Yes, and a charming piece. My not being able to get rid of you involuntarily made me think of the play; and since you assure me that Schootmanns really exists, it is quite clear that the author took you as his model for the character of the typically persistent commercial traveler."

My visitor looked taken aback at last. He twirled his little mustache, and stammered:

" I'm really sorry, very sorry——"

I opened the door. He was outside at last. The fresh air seemed to revive him and to give him back his power of speech, for just as I was about to close the door he turned to me with a smile:

" Oh, yes, I forgot the champagne. We have an excellent brand, Marquis de——"

I heard no more, for I slammed the door so hard that all the lamps and windows in the building rattled.

I never saw the representative of Kolik & Co. again.

The Ex-pirate

" But, conductor, that is first class, for non-smokers."

" Second class is all full."

" Well, but my ticket is for the second class!"

" Please get in, my dear la—, woman," said the conductor, to whom the passenger seemed too common-looking to be addressed as " lady." " If you please, we are just going to start."

" I hope I'll see you again very soon, my dear," said the woman, and nodded to a little girl who, laden with parcels and packages, was standing on the platform. " Give my love to all at home—do you hear, child? And now hand me my hat-box, please, and the little basket and the large basket, will you?"

The first whistle for departure blew.

" Yes, yes! But, heavens, how high!" moaned the corpulent woman. With her left hand she grasped the door of the compartment and struggled violently to get in. Her right hand held an umbrella and a little traveling-bag, and under her left arm she crushed a pasteboard box.

" All in?" sounded the stentorian voice of the station-master. The doors of the last compartments shut with a bang.

"Ready!"

"No, not yet. Oh, what am I to do?" groaned the stout old woman, caught half-way in the door.

"So—there you are!" the conductor laughed, as he pushed the rest of her in.

"Now my hat-box! Thank you, my dear. And now the large basket—don't forget to give my love to all—and now the little basket. Is it shut tight? And, child, don't forget to take care of the cat and feed the canary."

"All in? Back there, if you please!"

"My child"—the head bobbed out of the window once more—"don't forget to have the empty preserve-bottles returned."

The second whistle blew, the train started, and the last words were lost in the rattle of wheels.

"Good heavens, what a rush!" sighed the woman, quite out of breath, sitting down next to the only other passenger, who was just preparing for a nap. "Oh, dear! Oh, dear!"

"For Heaven's sake, what's the matter?" growled the traveler, resenting this disturbance.

"Oh, you were going to sleep? Then you'll be so good as to pardon me. In the noise and hurry I overlooked you. Don't you think this train bumps dreadfully?"

"I? Yes—no—I don't know." And then the other passenger settled back in his corner and closed his eyes.

"This is a shame, though!" complained the woman, as she tried in vain to force all her various belongings into the rack over her head. "Oh, goodness gracious! I hope you don't mind. It's really not my fault. It's only the chestnuts for my brother-in-law's children. They dote on them so. I hope you aren't hurt! But it's so hard to get the things up there."

"Well, perhaps it would be better if you put that bag in the rack on the other side. It might fall again, you know."

"You're quite right, to be sure. You might have been badly hurt. It's a good thing you got off so easily."

The traveler pushed his cap back a little, stroked his back hair with his one hand, and looked half angrily, half sleepily at the stout woman, who, smiling at him with foolish good nature over her spectacles, said, "I suppose you're tired of the journey?" Then she went on in a loud voice, "But gracious me, now that I look at you more closely, why, I know you!"

"You? Me!" the traveler exclaimed.

"Yes; your name is Bolders, and you belong to the clothing-shop in the Hoogstraat."

"Sorry, but I don't happen to be that gentleman."

"What a pity! You see, I could have sworn you were Bolders. But if you yourself say that you are not he, I suppose it's all right. But is it possible? You have the same appearance exactly as Jan Bolders. And yet, when I look closely I see the difference. All the Bolders are red-haired, and you are quite fair."

The traveler yawned, and glared at his neighbor.

"But the thick nose of the Bolders—you have that. What a strange coincidence!"

"My name is van Palen, and I am sleepy." The voice was angry and curt. Once more he closed his eyes, and again settled himself comfortably to continue his nap.

The woman started up in astonishment. "Your name is van Palen! How strange! Then you are related to the van Palens of Rotterdam? Just think, I've known them for years, and I was great friends with Cato van Palen—your aunt, probably—a good-natured person, but so troubled with nerves that finally we got angry at each other. Is she still alive?"

An inarticulate grunt silenced the old woman for a moment.

"No? Well, I'd be sorry in spite of it all. I suppose you mean the van Palens van de Wynhaven?"

The same grunt.

"But perhaps you are related to the van Palens van de Baan? I know them too. Charming people!"

"No; I have no relatives."

"Not one?"

"No; I'm an orphan, and I'd like to sleep now."

"An orphan? I suppose you were brought up in an asylum. How very sad! I have always pitied the poor little orphans so! Of course they're well treated in the asylums, but they have to eat beans and peas so often. That isn't particularly nourishing, and it makes one so stout. And, after all, it isn't like home. Who'd ever believe that you were a little orphan boy once! You don't look it at all— so stylish, and traveling first class. The Lord has been good to you. You see, I'm just a plain burgher's wife, but I have all I want. Yet I always travel third class, but to-day everything was crowded. Goodness, how fast this train is going! There are only a few stops before Rotterdam, eh? One at Nieuwersluis——"

"Quite right. Thank Heaven, we do stop at Nieuwersluis!" said the other traveler, quite nervous from the woman's persistent chatter. He had yawned several times, and looked very sleepy, but now he sat up, measured his neighbor over from head to foot with an ironical smile, and began in a voice full of emotion:

Justus van Maurik

"I suppose you have a good heart. One can see it in your pity for the sorrow of the wretched orphans. Is that not so?"

The woman nodded slowly and with dignity. "So you never knew either mother or father?"

"Never," said the man with a suppressed sob. "My father died before my birth, and my good mother too!" He seemed deeply moved, and hid his face in his handkerchief.

"How sad! How very, very sad!" said the stout woman, and wiped away a tear.

"When I was three years old I went to sea."

"To sea?"

"Yes, I had to."

"Gracious!"

"I was stolen out of my cradle!"

"What?"

"Stolen!"

"Merciful heavens! and who did it?"

"A servant-girl who had a love-affair with a pirate."

"Oh, dearie me! And why did the girl do it?"

"Because she had no child, and the pirate wanted one."

"You don't say so! Oh, the curious things that happen in this world!"

"But, you see, this pirate was very fond of children."

"So it seems. But didn't he rob and murder?"

"Certainly. Every one he captured he had hanged or shot, but he spared the innocent little ones. We had one pirate on board who had nothing to do but fill bottles with milk for the infants."

"And what became of the mothers?"

Dutch Wit and Humor

" If they were young and good-looking, the pirate put them into his harem. If they were plain and elderly, they were exposed on desert islands, or butchered on board."

" Butchered? But that is awful! And you saw it all with your own eyes? "

" Yes, from my tenderest years I was a witness of human slaughter. When I was thirteen I stood the test by killing two missionaries."

" Killing! " The fat old person got as far away from her neighbor as possible.

" Yes; and not with a dagger or pistol. I simply poured something into their coffee."

" Oh! "

" Yes, it was easy. They noticed nothing, and ten minutes later they were in heaven."

His corpulent traveling companion grew pale, wide-eyed, and open-mouthed. The man went on calmly:

" After a while I became a perfect monster. I have a thirst for blood. With this little instrument, you see "—he pulled out a small pocket-knife—" I have sent at least a hundred and fifty people to a better land. They used to call me the ' Terror of the Sea.' "

" With that little knife? " She was almost choked with fright.

" Yes. One skilful cut—the vein is severed—and there you are—dead! But I was converted two years ago."

" Oh! How? "

" By the Salvation Army in New York; and now remorse tortures me for all the blood I have spilled."

The good-natured woman almost panted. She kept her eyes fixed on his hands. With trembling voice she asked:

" And now you have given up piracy altogether? "

"Yes, and it's a pity. My profession was a pleasant one
—small expenses and large income."

"Yes, and——"

"I understand. You want to know what I do now. Well,
I have a good deal to do with corpses now."

This made the good woman feel more comfortable.

"I suppose you're an undertaker."

"A what? Oh, no; you are mightily mistaken. I procure corpses for the dissecting-rooms of the professors of
medicine."

A sudden trembling shook the great mass of flesh.

"And how do you procure them?"

"Oh, very simply; I buy them, dig them up, or make
them."

"God help me, but that's horrible!" Heavy beads of per-
spiration rolled from her forehead.

The traveler went on in an icy tone:

"There are always people enough who are willing to sell
some old uncle or aunt, if they get money enough; and I have
no end of money."

"But—but, then, why do you do it?"

"Mere sport, my dear woman—mere sport! I'm so accustomed to blood and corpses."

"Wha-a-at?"

"Oh, yes. To-day, for instance, I'm going from Em-
merich to Rotterdam to buy an old woman—unfortunately
only one, and I need two for Professor Ralph of London. I
have given my word of honor to get him two large females
between fifty and sixty years of age."

The uncanny individual let his hand glide into his pocket.

"Perhaps it's sensible to take the first safe chance. Do
you care very much about living longer?"

The woman jumped up. Speechless, she stared at the man. "Nieuwersluis!" The door flew open.

"Nieuwersluis!"

The woman in her terrible excitement had not noticed that the train was slowing up. Hardly was the door open, than she trundled out of it like a rubber ball, and screamed:

"Conductor! I want to get into a different compartment. Quick! take my hat-box! There's a pirate in here—please get my traveling-bag—a fellow who makes corpses! Heavens! My chestnuts—a hundred and fifty murders on his conscience! But no children. Oh, my umbrella! He wants stout corpses. Yes, yes, I'll get into the luggage-van! I'm fainting! The monster!"

The traveler once more settled into his corner. "Conductor," he said, "here's something for yourself—and a cigar. Please see to it that I am not disturbed; I want to get some sleep."

Hungarian Wit and Humor

Maurus Jókai

The Feat of Swallowing a Mouse

THE nabob suddenly turned toward the landlord:

"Have you a mouse on the premises?"

"They are not mine, my Lord; I only rent the house. But as there are plenty of them, I don't suppose the ground landlord will begin an action at law if I take one or two."

"Then roast us a mouse."

"Only one?"

"Plague on such a question! Do you take the belly of a man for the abyss of hell, to think that one such beast is not quite enough for it?"

"At your service, my Lord," said the innkeeper; and he immediately called the cats into the room to assist him, though he had only to move a few stones away in order to be able to pick and choose his mouse quite as well as any cat could have done it for him.

And here I may say, by the way, that a mouse is such a nice, pretty little animal, that I cannot conceive why folks should hold it in such horror. It is very much the same thing as a squirrel or a guinea-pig, which we keep in our rooms and pet and play with; nay, it is cleverer far than they. What a delicate little snout it has, what sweet little ears, what wee little pets of feet! And then, its comically big mustache, and its quick black eyes like sparkling diamonds! And when it plays, when it squeaks, when it stands up to beat the air on its hind legs, it is as clever and as comely as any other animal in the world. Nobody is horrified at a crab being cooked, nobody flies in terror when snails are served up at table, yet they are both far more horrible animals than a mouse. What, then, is there so horrifying in the idea of cooking a mouse? Why, in China it is the greatest of delicacies, a lordly dish for epicures, and they fatten it in cages with nuts and almonds, and serve it up as the choicest of savories.

Nevertheless, the whole company was persuaded that the very idea of such a thing was the most exquisite of jokes, and every one laughed aloud in anticipation.

Meanwhile, while Peter Bús threw open a large barn-like room for his guests, the lackeys had unpacked the wagon, and dragged into the light of day cushions, curtains, camp-stools, and tables; and in a few moments the empty, resonant room was changed as if by magic into a sumptuous apartment. The table was piled high with silver goblets and dishes, and, reposing among the ice in large silver pitchers, flasks of carved Venetian crystal with long necks seemed to promise something seductive.

The nabob himself lay down on the camp-bedstead prepared for him, his lackeys drew the large spurred boots from his feet, one of the peasant-girls sat by his head stroking continually his sparse gray hairs, while the other sat at the end of the bed rubbing his feet with bits of flannel. Gyárfás, the poet, and Vidra, the jester, stood before him; a little farther off the lackeys; the greyhound was under the bed. And thus, surrounded by gipsy, lackeys, jester, peasant-girls, and greyhound, lay one of the wealthiest magnates of Hungary.

Meanwhile the mouse was a-roasting. The innkeeper himself brought it, lying in the middle of a large silver dish, surrounded by a heap of horseradish shavings, and with a bit of green parsley in its mouth, the usual appurtenances of a very different animal.

Down it was placed in the middle of the table.

First of all, the nabob offered it to the lackeys one by one. They did not fancy it, and only shook their heads.

Then it came to the poet's turn.

"Pardon, your Excellency! I am composing verses on him who eats it."

"Well, you, then, Vidra! Come, down with it, quick!"

"I, your Excellency?" said Vidra, as if he did not quite catch the words.

"Yes, you. What are you afraid of? While you were living in tents, one of my oxen went mad, and yet you and your people ate him."

"True; and if one of your Lordship's hogsheads of wine went mad I would drink it. That's another thing."

"Come, come, make haste! Do the dish honor."

"But my grandfather had no quarrel with this animal."

"Then rise superior to your grandpapa."

"I'll rise superior to him for a hundred Gulden," said the gipsy, scratching his curly poll.

The nobleman opened the pocket of his jacket and drew forth a large greasy pocketbook, which he half opened, displaying a number of nice blood-colored bank-notes.

The gipsy squinted with half an eye at the well-crammed pocketbook, and repeated once more:

"For a hundred Gulden I don't mind doing it."

"Let us see, then!"

The gipsy thereupon unbuttoned the frock coat which it was his master's whim he should wear, contracted his rotund, foolish face into a squarish shape, twitched the mobile skin of his head up and down once or twice, whereby the whole forest of his hair moved backward and forward like the topknot of a pewit, and then, seizing the horrible animal by that part of its body which was farthest from its head, and thereby raising it into the air, pulled an ugly, acidulous face, shook his head, constrained himself to a desperate resolution, opened his mouth, shut his eyes, and in an instant the mouse had disappeared.

The gipsy could not speak, but one of his hands involuntarily clutched his throat, for it is no joke to swallow a four-legged animal at a gulp; but his other hand he extended toward the nabob, gasping with something like a sob:

"The hundred Gulden!"

"What hundred Gulden?" inquired the humorous nobleman. "I said I'd give you a hundred Gulden? Nonsense, sir. You should thank me for providing you with such a rare dish, which your grandfather never ate, I'll be bound to say, and would have paid for the chance of it."

It was a screaming joke, no doubt; yet suddenly the merriment ceased, for the gipsy all at once began to turn blue and green, his eyes threatened to start out of his head, he sank down on his chair unable to speak, but pointed convulsively to his distended mouth.

"Look, look! He's choking!" cried several voices.

The nabob was terribly alarmed. The joke had taken a decidedly serious turn.

"Pour wine into his throat to wash it down!" he exclaimed.

The lackeys speedily caught up the flasks and began to fill up the gipsy's throat with half a bottle at a time, to assist the downward progress of the worthy mouse. After a long time the poor fellow began to breathe hard, and seemed to

recover slightly; but his eyes rolled wildly, and he was gab-
bling something unintelligible.

"Well, take your hundred Gulden," said the frightened
magnate, who could scarcely contain himself for terror, and
wished to comfort and compensate the gipsy on his return
from Charon's ferry-boat.

"Thank you," sobbed the other, "but there's no need of
it now. It is all up with Vidra; Vidra is dying. If only it
had been a wolf that had killed poor Vidra; but a mouse—
oh, oh!"

"Don't be a fool, man! You'll take no harm from it.
Look! here's another hundred. Don't take on so; it has
quite gone now. Hit him on the back, some one, can't you?
Bring the venison on now, and make him swallow some
of it!"

The jester thanked them for the thump on the back, and
when they set the venison before him, he regarded it with
the doubtful, ambiguous expression of a spoiled child, who
does not know whether to laugh or to cry. First he laughed,
and then he grumbled again, but finally he sat him down
before the savory cold meat, which had been basted with the
finest lard and flavored with good cream-like wine sauce, and
began to cram himself full with morsel after morsel so huge
that there was surely never a mouse in the wide world half
so big. And thus he not only filled himself, but satisfied the
nabob also.

And now, at a sign from the nabob, the lackeys carried
in all the cold dishes they had brought with them, and shoved
the loaded table along till it stood opposite the couch on
which he lay. At the lower end of the table three camp-
stools were placed, and on them sat the three favorites—the
jester, the greyhound, and the poet. The magnate gradually

acquired an appetite by watching these three creatures eat, and by degrees the wine put them all on the most familiar terms with one another, the poet beginning to call the gipsy "my Lord," while the gipsy metaphorically buttonholed the nabob, who scattered petty witticisms on the subject of the mouse, whereat the two others were obliged to laugh with all their might.

At last, when the worthy gentleman really believed that it was quite impossible to play any more variations on the well-worn topic of the mouse, the gipsy suddenly put his hand to his bosom, and cried with a laugh, " Here's the mouse ! " And with that he drew it forth from the inside pocket of his frock coat, where he had shoved it unobserved, while the terrified company fancied he had swallowed it, and in sheer despair had soothed him by making him eat and drink all manner of good things.

" Look, Mat ! " said he to the dog, whereupon the grey-hound immediately swallowed the *corpus delicti.*

" You good-for-nothing rascal ! " cried the nobleman, " so you'd bandy jests with me, would you ! I'll have you hanged for this. Here, you lackeys, fetch a rope ! Hoist him upon that beam ! "

The lackeys immediately took their master at his word. They seized the gipsy, who never ceased laughing, mounted him on a chair, threw the halter round his neck, drew the extreme end of the rope across the beam, and drew away the chair from beneath him. The gipsy kicked and struggled, but it was of no avail; there they kept him till he really began to choke, when they lowered him to the ground again.

But now he began to be angry. " I am dying," he cried. " I am not a fool, that you should hoist me up again, when I can die as I am, like an honest gentleman."

Maurus Jókai

" Die, by all means," said the poet. " Don't be afraid. I'll think of an epitaph for you."

And while the gipsy flung himself on the ground and closed his eyes, Gyárfás recited this epitaph over him:

" Here liest thou, gipsy-lad, never to laugh any longer ;
  Another shall shoulder the fiddle, and death shall himself fiddle
  o'er thee."

And, in fact, the gipsy never moved a limb. There he lay, prone, stiff, and breathless. In vain they tickled his nose and his heels; he did not stir. Then they placed him on the table with a circle of burning candles round him, like one laid out for burial, and the lackeys had to sing dirges over him, as over a corpse, while the poet was obliged to stand upon a chair and pronounce his funeral oration.

And the nabob laughed till he got blue in the face.

—" A Hungarian Nabob."

Alexander Balázs

My Double

I HAVE a certain acquaintance whom, to my sincere regret,
I meet very seldom. Frankly, I should like to be with him
often—if possible, daily. In the first place, because he is a
very cultivated and charming person, with whom one can
gossip away a most delightful hour over a glass of beer or a
bottle of wine. The second reason is, that whenever we
meet he gives me a cigar that costs at least a gulden. If
I make any motion to refuse it, he knows how to overcome
my scruples with so much delicacy, to convince me so thoroughly that my acceptance would confer a favor upon him,
that I at last incline to his view of the case, and light his
fragrant Havana. Any one who is as passionately fond of
smoking as I will not blame me for not pushing refusal to
the point of quixotism. Furthermore, we live in a civilized
society; we are not barbarians. Courtesy is a duty, a virtue,
and demands of us that we yield to the wishes of our fellow
men. Hence I may confess, without endangering my reputation, that I am not sorry to receive cigars costing a Gulden,
but, that silently I rather cherish the wish to meet my
acquaintance and his cigars daily.

My acquaintance! Ah, what is his name? Now I have
even forgotten his name. What ingratitude! By way of
excuse I can only allege that this forgetfulness is the fault
not of my heart, but of my memory. And then it is, in a
measure, his own fault; for it is certain that his name is
one of such frequent occurrence as to have little of specific

and only a generic value—Smith, or Brown, or Robinson. But this is not the worst. Not only have I forgotten his name, but I have no idea of his occupation. I only know that he must be master of a considerable income, for his purse is exceedingly well filled whenever one sees him. Then, too, it is no small matter not only to smoke cigars at a Gulden, but to offer them to one's acquaintances. No member of the middle class could do it. And so I have no idea who he is or what is his position in society. Nor shall I ever know. We have no acquaintances in common, and I would not commit the indiscretion of questioning him. It is noticeable that he not only offers me cigars worth a Gulden, but never omits to mention this latter fact, from which I infer that he is a Philistine or an upstart. But it is useless to dwell on this point. The fact remains that his cigars are excellent, and that I regret not meeting him oftener.

Another fact about my anonymous acquaintance has struck me. Whenever we meet I have to listen to the same complaint from him. At our first meeting he started it, and whenever we see each other he begins the same story, so that I am inclined to think it has become a fixed idea with him. He expresses his regret that we have not met for so long a time, offers me a cigar, and plunges into the tale of his grievance.

" Just consider what wretched bad luck I have ! The thing is unheard-of, and could have happened only to me."

" You don't say so ! "

" Just think, there is a fellow in this town who bears so extraordinary a resemblance to me, not only in feature, but in gesture and speech, that no one can possibly distinguish us from each other."

Hungarian Wit and Humor

" Dear me, how astonishing ! "

" So complete is the resemblance that my own mother could not tell me from him. I once had an interview with my double, and discovered from him that he had been born not only in the same year, and on the same day, but at the very same hour as myself."

" Such a resemblance is amazing; but why should you consider it a peculiar misfortune ? "

" What ! do you not see that I am held responsible for all the behavior of a complete stranger ? "

" You are right; that is pretty bad."

" It's worse than that; it is a positive misfortune. I have to live in continual terror of being arrested for theft or forgery or burglary, or of being pursued by a cast-off mistress who may scratch my eyes out and throw acid in my face. One day a tailor attacked me on the street because I had not paid him a debt of ten Gulden. In vain I assured him that I did not owe him anything, that he was taking me for some one else. He grew angrier and more scandalous in his behavior, and so, in order to avoid a street row, I had to pay my wretched double's debt."

" And why did you not call upon the police for help ? "

" Do you think I wanted to make a public exhibition of myself ? The enraged tailor bawled so that all the passers-by stopped. Oh, it was horrible ! I shall go mad in the end, or commit suicide."

" And what sort of a person is your double ? "

" A rascal, a drunkard, a rake, a wretched creature, who, though he dresses in rags and prowls about the lowest rum-shops, has the audacity to accost respectable girls in order to seduce them. The whole affair is no joke, I assure you, but a very real misfortune. I tremble when I think of the misunderstandings that I might be plunged into in the social circles where I move."

"My dear sir, surely you exaggerate. Your friends and social connections know you too well to associate you with the vile conduct of another, no matter what his resemblance to you may be."

"You are very innocent, and know little of the world. The majority of men do not recoil from slander, and are willing to believe the worst, rather than the best, of their fellow men. But the worst thing that I have to anticipate is that one fine day my betrothed may suddenly meet this man with some vulgar trollop."

"I would advise you to pay him to leave town."

"I have tried that too. I once met him in a suburb, and asked him to dine with me. He accepted, saying that he was glad to make my more intimate acquaintance. I then discovered that he was a sign-painter by trade. I offered him a thousand Gulden if he would leave the capital. He refused with scorn. He liked city life, he said, and would rather be a beggar here than a king elsewhere. So you see the hopelessness of my situation."

Thus I have to hear his story and his jeremiads about it. I acknowledge that he never forgets to offer me his excellent cigars, and I am weak enough to accept them, even at the risk of hearing the same story over again. I had not seen him for a long time once, and I began to believe that he had emigrated, or died, when I met him quite accidentally on the street. He was walking in front of me, and I was just then in a state of mind in which a Havana cigar would have been very grateful to me. I therefore tried to catch him up, but just as I was about to succeed, he turned and entered a house. When I returned, somewhat later, by the same road,

Hungarian Wit and Humor

I saw my acquaintance emerging from the same house. But what a change had taken place in him! Instead of the well-cut clothes which he ordinarily affected, he was garbed in rags; instead of his gleaming silk hat, he wore a common working-man's cap. And yet it was he himself, and no other, no painter who bore a close resemblance to him. No resemblance *could* be so absolute. And yet, did he not say that his own mother could not tell him from his double? I did not know whether to address him or not. Curiosity conquering me, I approached him, smiled, and said, " Good morning, friend." He stopped in surprise. Then he said, in a hoarse voice:

" What can I do for you? I have not the honor of your acquaintance."

" I beg your pardon," I said, " I must have been mistaken."

" I thought so," he answered; " the same thing has happened to me before."

I was overwhelmed with astonishment. My anonymous friend was right. Never had there been such a resemblance. At that moment some one called to me, patted my shoulder familiarly, and when I turned around I recognized my old friend B., the police lieutenant.

" What are you staring at? " he asked.

I told him the whole story.

" I understand," he said, " and I know your double and his excellent cigars quite well."

" Thank Heaven! My curiosity will be satisfied at last! Believe me, I am interested in the man for his own sake, not only for the sake of his cigars. But don't let us stand in the street. Here is a *café*."

I now heard the whole story. My acquaintance was a cunning and experienced adventurer, a Don Juan besides, and an irreclaimable gambler. Whenever he won heavily it was his habit to smoke cigars of at least a Gulden each. As soon as all his money was gone he changed back to the humble sign-painter, and worked until he had saved enough to start again. The story about his double was a trick to disarm the suspicion of his acquaintances, should they meet him in his working-man's costume. At last the police found him out, and kept a vigilant eye on him.

Now I should like to know when I shall ever again have the pleasure of smoking cigars at a Gulden each?

Árpád Berczik

An Expensive Marriage

ONE fine day I saw on the street pavement two absurdly
small feet. I am a born esthete, and since there is more of
the esthetic to be found in such a little pair of feet than in
a dozen folios, and as I prefer experimental to theoretical
science, there was nothing left for me to do but to follow
the pair of feet. They hopped and scudded rapidly. I kept
up with them. A woman selling crockery sits in my way;
I stumble over her wares and smash a lot of them. She is
enraged, and cries for vengeance. She throws herself upon
me. I throw her a bank-bill. I believe it was one for ten
Gulden. Let us say ten Gulden.

That quieted things. My pursuer cooled off, and I was
able to continue my own pursuit. I sought earnestly for my
little feet—that is, her little feet (not the crockery woman's).
There they are again. At the same moment she who owns
the little feet turns round and looks at me. She floats up
to a cab and gets into it. I take another. She drives off, with
me after her.

This drive, together with a liberal tip for racing time, costs
five Gulden. Our cabbies raced each other. She stopped
in front of a fashionable shop. She entered it. Need I say
that I did the same? Our actions were nearly simultaneous.
In the shop she looked at me in surprise—from tip to toe.
Then I was richer by another experience, for her face surpassed her feet in beauty, and her figure her face.

The shopkeeper looked at me questioningly, and asked,
" What can I do for you? "

Árpád Berczik

Near me sounds a voice like a little silver bell, "Please show me your silks."

The sound of her voice electrifies me. Thus must the angels sing at Christmas-tide.

Of course I say, "Please show me your silks."

"What color?"

Her hair and eyes are black. "Black," then.

Thereupon the lovely stranger looked at me again. Something passed over her face. What it was, and why it passed, I do not know. I did not worry much, so deeply was I engrossed in that fairy form handling the silks.

The shopkeeper—that horrible shopkeeper! How he tortured me with questions! Is this a cross-examination? Let him give me what he chooses, wrap it up and hand me the bill, but, above all, leave me in peace to contemplate my haggling goddess. Do you not understand, my good man, why I am here? What do I care for your wares, or their quality or price? My visit here is due to her little feet, her little head, her figure!

At last my purchase was concluded. Not so hers. She still haggles. And this unnatural monster of a shopkeeper does not kneel down before her, and cry, "All I have I lay down at your feet, only suffer me to love you!" Instead of doing that, he smiles, and refuses to reduce his price. The miserable creature says something about fixed prices, and at last gains his point. In order to be present at this painful scene to its very end, I was obliged to buy some other things. A nice way of passing one's time! My bundles grew infinite, and when I had them carried out to my cab a curious smile played about the fair lady's mouth. My bill at the shop mounts up to two hundred and fifty Gulden!

We got into our cabs and drove on. Suddenly mine stops.

What has happened? We have killed an old woman's little pet pug. The old wretch raises an alarm, so that my driver has to stop. She curses, and demands damages for the life of the murdered innocent. A crowd gathers. My fair lady's vehicle is almost out of sight. An idea! I plunge into my pocket, and throws its contents to the owner of the pug. The crowd scrambles for the coins. I cry, "Drive on!" I am saved.

I had thrown about eight Gulden out of the window. Thus we catch up the cab of my fairy. Her cab stops before a house. She gets out and enters the door. A quarter of an hour passes, half an hour—three hours! She does not return, neither does any one come for her bundles. It is merely a visit. And so, while she is having a pleasant time within, I am bored to death, and freeze like a Congo negro in Siberia, for it is winter. I take refuge in a confectionary-shop opposite the house that I must watch. The shop-girls notice the bundles on my cab, and I take the opportunity of getting rid of my purchases by presenting them to the young women. One of them at once hurries out, and loads herself with packages, when, oh, fate! my enchantress issues from the door opposite.

Next day things took a surprising turn. It appeared that my man was courting the maid servant of my fair unknown. He gave me very exact information. Her name is Szánfalvay. She is a widow. For the word *widow* my man got ten Gulden as a present. Furthermore, I increased his wages five Gulden per month. This comes to sixty Gulden a year. To her servant—Juczi is the girl's name—I gave ten Gulden. I obtained fairly precise information as to the society in which the lady moved, and intended to seek an introduction to her at the house of some common acquaintance; but a fortnight passed before I found an opportunity. During that time, in order to forget my grief, I spent at least two hundred Gulden more than usual.

My condition began to annoy me. My patience was at an end. Jancsi, my faithful servant, noticed it:

"You seem to take it to heart, sir, that you can't make the lady's acquaintance. What will you give me if I bring it about?"

"Listen, Jancsi; even impudence has its limits. If a servant gets too familiar, he goes!"

"I do not wish to be familiar. I am sorry for you, sir. You are getting thinner every day, so that I have to take all your clothes to the tailor's to have them made smaller."

The man spoke in a voice of genuine sympathy. What if he could really help me?

"Well, Jancsi, on the day that the lady receives me, you shall receive a hundred Gulden."

Three days later Jancsi handed me a little note. It came from the widow, and ran thus:

"I shall be glad if you will call on me at half past twelve to-day."

I very nearly hugged Jancsi. What a splendid fellow!

"How did you manage it?"

"That is my secret, with your permission. All you have to do is to be punctual."

In my joy I gave him the hundred Gulden.

At last I was ready to go. At the very moment set I rang the electric bell at the lady's house.

Juczi opened the door. She seemed excited, and received me with visible delight. I gave her ten Gulden. Scarcely had I entered the reception-room, when she came—the angel, the goddess! I should have liked to fall at her feet, but I restrained myself.

"You will pardon me—" said I.

She interrupted me. If I had not taken the first step, she says, she would have been obliged to do so.

Heavens! Is it possible?

"The affair is one that interests us both."

Affair! She calls it an affair!

"And so you know?"

"How should I not? Jancsi told Juczi, and Juczi told me——"

"And you do not object to it?"

"One should not stand in the way of true love. I consent to a marriage."

"To marriage?"

"Yes, and here is my hand upon it."

She gave me her little hand. I fell to my knees before her.

"Oh, I thank you, I thank you!"

The lady stepped back a little.

"What do you mean? Why do you thank me?"

"Because you give me your hand and consent to our marriage."

"*Our* marriage? Why, whoever put that into your head?"

"Well, then, who is to marry?"

"Why, Jancsi and Juczi. I am the girl's godmother, and so you were to get my consent!"

"And that was the reason you asked me to call?"

"Certainly. I am sorry that I cannot continue your acquaintance, for I am going to marry and move away to another place next week."

Who made a fool of me? Jancsi or the lady, or both?

The adventure cost me, all told—I prefer to let some one else do the sum.

Viktor Rákosi—"Sipulus"

The Alligator

ONE morning, when some of the keepers of the zoological
gardens went into the alligator's cave, they found protruding
from the animal's jaws an elegantly dressed leg, and a foot
clad in a patent-leather boot. They pulled at the leg and
extracted a man; and it was none other than Alfons Csokor,
the bank cashier, who was wont to spend his leisure hours
inspecting the animals.

The alligator had been his favorite. He had fed it with
buns, petted it, and finally established so close an intimacy
with it that he would have entrusted it with the key of the
cash-vault, which was under his care.

But one day that false friend ate him up, and they died of
it, both cashier and alligator. Half an hour later a man and
a woman were moaning in the alligator's cave. The woman
was the cashier's wife, the man was the alligator's keeper.

"You will never, never shed a tear again!" wailed the
keeper, and stroked the stiff scales.

"Who will take me to the Paris Exhibition?" sobbed the
woman.

"That he should go and swallow a cashier!" said the
keeper. "I'm sure I fed him very well. If he had only
chosen some one who was lean, whom he could have swallowed without choking!"

The end of all the weeping was that the widow brought a
suit for damages against the zoo. But the zoo, in its turn,
brought a counter-suit against the widow, on the ground that

an alligator is more valuable, and more difficult to procure, than a husband. The widow demanded the employment of expert testimony in the decision of these relative values. The government threatened a criminal investigation, in which several old alligators were to be brought up as witnesses. The authorities of the zoo declared that an alligator is an unintelligent animal; not so a cashier. It was therefore the latter's duty to see that he was not swallowed, not the former's to refrain (the opportunity being given) from swallowing.

At that time I was senior assistant in the law office of Dr. Bihalek, and my employer had entrusted the conduct of the case to me. We represented the widow. I protested against zoos in general, and alligators in particular, and described the widow's grief in such moving terms, that my employer said to me:

" Look here, Kondor, a novelist was lost in you. Did you ever try your hand at literature? "

" To be sure. I once translated a cook-book."

" Why did you not continue? "

" I am only taking a rest."

" To work, then; to work, young man! "

And so I began, taking as my central theme the alligator, for with the intricacies of this subject I was now thoroughly well acquainted. Another might have written a humorous novel on this subject, but in literature I was an adherent of realism; and, according to the custom of this school, I went straight for my subject, went for it without mercy. On every page of the novel there was some gloomy thought, on every other page a gross offense against good taste. Children defied their parents; young men fell in love with their mothers-in-law; the houses were all dirty, and in them not a single healthy human being could be found. Those were most fortunate who became insane. I was very proud of the novel, for I felt sure it would be forbidden in Austria, but would run through fifty editions in France. Upon the story proper I did not expend much effort, but treated with compensating fulness the inner life of the man, the woman, and the alligator. Whenever my flow of thought weakened, I would introduce endless irrelevant matter. There was a description of the building of a house that occupied a hundred pages.

When at last the work was complete, I went to submit it to a famous publisher known to be in sympathy with the realistic school. He asked me whether my novel was bad. With a modest smile I answered:

"On the contrary, I believe it is good, and will excite attention."

"Then I can find no use for it."

"No use for a good novel?"

"I should like to well enough, but the public won't have it. People are deadly sick of these 'good' novels. The critics praise them, but no one buys them. But I tell you what you might do: write a bad novel."

"By which you mean?"

"Here is a recipe. A couple of suicides, faithless women, perjured men, a great deal of myth, and a handful of secrets. I'll have it illustrated, and print it in instalments at fifteen Kreutzers apiece."

I consented to this plan, and wrote a blood-and-thunder story of the worst kind. I described the director of the zoo as an enemy of mankind, who imported the man-eating alligators of the Nile for his evil purposes. I depicted the widow as a scandalous flirt who drove her husband to death—

that is, into the alligator—by her faithlessness. Her husband was represented, of course, as a defaulting cashier. At the beginning of each instalment there was a picture, and what a picture! A dark night—a street corner—a man with somber cloak and dagger drawn! At the fifth instalment the widow sued me; at the sixth the director of the zoo.

My situation was comic enough. I was to buy the zoo a new alligator, and marry the widow. Upon these conditions alone was I to be forgiven, and the suit discontinued. Yes, there was a third condition: I was to discontinue my novel. But the instalments were sold in editions of twenty thousand, and I would have been a fool to discontinue it. Hence I married the widow. So she forgave me the libel, and, since she had a new husband, she forgave the zoo, which in turn forgave me.

The zoo still had no new alligator, and still held my wife responsible for the loss.

One day, taking part by chance in a great raffling and drawing of lots at the zoo, I won an elephant. I magnanimously presented the elephant to the zoo, which consented to cancel its claim against my wife.

I am now a happy man and novelist, but fearful suspicions arise in me whenever my wife proposes a walk in the zoo.

The Summer Outing

I BELONG to those inhabitants of Budapest who must spend the summer in the country on pain of not being received back into society in autumn. Heaven is my witness that I would rather remain in Budapest, and not depart by a hair's breadth from my accustomed ways; but at the very beginning of summer my wife watches how many blinds are down in the neighborhood, indicating that people have gone away for the summer. Then the little woman gets hold of me, smiles her sweetest smile, and says, "My dear, bring home a few pounds of moth-powder." As soon as the children hear this they skip with delight, and cry, "Now we're going to the country! Papa is going out for powder!"

Our stay in the country is preceded by an enormous washing of linen, a cleaning up of unheard-of dimensions, and a failure of the children's appetite. My children do their mother the favor of looking pale and delicate at the very beginning of the summer. If they look so in winter I am accused of surreptitiously feeding them on sweets; but in summer they are held to be accustomed to that unhealthy diet. What they need is change of air. "The doctor says so too!"

The doctor! Before that mandate all husbands are helpless. Of course, the doctor sends all his patients away, in order that he may himself go.

My wife carefully reads the newspaper accounts of the city's health, but only in early summer. Thus, at breakfast she can tell me just how many cases of measles and diphtheria there are in the town, and how many of these have resulted fatally. Then she pets the children, and says, "If only we were out of this unhealthy town!"

One day a new disease was reported in the paper. My wife exclaimed: "Frightful! A new disease, and all who got it have died of it."

I looked into the paper. One case was reported, and that had indeed ended fatally. Such is the mind of woman.

To avoid any misunderstanding, I wish to add that I never,

by word or act, give my wife reason to think that we are not going on our trip. It was an unbroken custom of ours to go. . . .

One year we went to a very fashionable Hungarian resort. There I had to fight four duels: one with a gentleman who stared at my wife, one with a gentleman at whose wife I stared, the third with the physician of the place, who gathered practise by forcing duels on the guests, and the fourth with the director of the place, because I remarked on the poor quality of the food.

The next year we went to a watering-place of the second class. There was nothing to eat and drink but bitter cheese and sweet milk. Furthermore, the town had a dispute with the manager of the summer hotel, and so the farmers drove their cattle across the promenade. Two months it was the chief business of my life to fight cows, and to this day if I meet a cow I give her a push, and if a cow meets me she runs.

The next summer we tried Budakezs. But there the guests held a fair every night for the benefit of Suabian children, for whom boots and shoes were to be procured, although they looked upon the articles with increased mistrust. . . .

And then in the autumn we come back, worn out, to our dear old Budapest, and sing the praises of our summer resort so vigorously that in the course of a fortnight we really begin to believe we have had a good time.

During the third week we commence reviling the capital, and next summer we flee to the country again.

Dalmatian Wit and Humor

Traditional Legend

The Doge's Daughter

In one of the many castles formerly standing on the shores of the Adriatic Sea there lived the daughter of a doge of Venice. Her godmother was a fairy of the mountains, who had showered upon her all the most precious gifts. She had given her marvelous beauty, and had promised her in marriage the handsomest and noblest of men. The doge's wife had taken every precaution that her daughter should not forget these predictions. She had placed in Zora's chamber two chaffinches in a cage. She had taught these birds to repeat a little song, in which Zora was compared to the sun, the moon, and all sorts of stars, and which declared that she must choose a husband as handsome among men as she was beautiful among women.

And, in truth, when Zora was eighteen years of age she was the most lovely and exquisite of all creatures. Her father gave her for her dowry enormous treasures of gold and silver, and the two islands of Cyprus and Rhodes, with their harbors, fortresses, and storehouses filled with merchandise, and vessels innumerable. Thus Zora was certain not to lack suitors; indeed, it was not long before they began to arrive in crowds.

The first who came was the son of an emperor from beyond Stamboul. He was as shapely as a sculptured statue. Furthermore, he was a renowned hero who had defeated the Turks in a hundred battles. He brought magnificent presents, massive gold and glittering jewels. He laid at Zora's feet pearls of incredible splendor, which he had taken from the turban of a sultan of Arabia whom he had slain in a duel. Surely any girl might have been glad of such a husband. Zora gave him no more than a disdainful glance. She did not think him worthy of any courtesy. She sent one of her maids to tell him that she could not think of marrying so ugly and insignificant a person.

After she had thus repulsed this noble suitor, she ran weeping into the forest and called to her fairy godmother.

" What do you want, my little daughter? " asked the fairy, who had appeared suddenly, wearing a veil embroidered with gold and full of white roses. " Why do you sigh so, my darling? "

" What do I want? Why do I sigh? Did you not promise me that my husband should be the noblest and handsomest prince on earth? And now that the time has come when I might marry, you send me some emperor's son from Stamboul, a stupid soldier, who boasts coarsely of having killed his hundreds, who offers my parents gold and jewels, the commonest things in the world, and who dares offer me pearls from the turban of a sultan whom he has killed. If only he were good to look at. But his nose is bent and sharp-tipped, like the sickle of the moon. I shudder at the idea of having such a monster for a husband. Is this the way in which you keep your word? "

" Well, little daughter, the Emperor of Stamboul's son is really the handsomest and noblest of men. Still, if he does not please you, send him away."

" I did not wait for your advice to do that," said Zora; " I showed him the door."

" As you please," said the fairy; " but my intentions were good. I have evidently not found what you desire. But have patience. Other claimants for your hand will present themselves. I am only sorry for the white roses which I had prepared for your marriage-wreath, and which will now wither."

"What does it matter?" cried Zora. "I am in no haste. I would rather wait ten years than marry that crooked-nosed soldier." Then she went, and the fairy disappeared into the depths of the forest.

When Zora came back to the castle she learned that the emperor's son had already departed. But, since he did not care to have undertaken the long journey for nothing, he had immediately married the maid through whom Zora had informed him that he might return to Stamboul.

Some time passed, and another suitor presented himself at the castle. It was the son of the King of Caramania. He was handsome and accomplished, nor could any painter have depicted a face more fascinating than his. Furthermore, he was a scholar and a renowned poet. He brought Zora's parents magnificent presents of fine silver. At Zora's feet he laid a laurel crown, that had been awarded him in a great contest of poets.

Zora scarce gave him a look, turned her back upon him, and sent a maid to tell him he might depart instantly. It was in vain that he presented himself before her parents. Zora said she would never marry such a monster. Then she burst into tears, and ran off into the woods, calling for her fairy godmother. The latter appeared, and her embroidered veil was full of red roses.

"Why do you weep?"

"Why do I weep? First you send me a soldier with a crooked nose, and now, whom do you send to replace him? A pedant, a rimester, who knows of nothing but his books,

who has nothing to offer but silver, and a bit of laurel such
as one uses to flavor sauces. And then, his face! He has
not only a hooked nose, but a beard like a crowbar. Would
you have me marry such a monster? Is it thus that you
keep your word?"

"That I have," answered the fairy, "for the prince from
Caramania is really the handsomest and most gallant knight
now living. I have kept my word. Still, if he does not
please you, you can send him away."

"I have done so already."

"Very well, you need not force your inclination. I will
send you another, who will no doubt find favor in your eyes.
I am only sorry for these beautiful roses, which were to
form your nuptial crown, and which must now wither."

"What does it matter?" cried Zora. "Rather than marry
such a pedant, I would remain virgin for twenty years more."
She went away, and the fairy once more vanished into the
depths of the forest.

When Zora returned to the castle she learned that the
Caramanian prince had already departed, and that, out of
spite for her refusal, he had married the girl by whom Zora's
disdainful message had come to him, and that he had carried
off his bride on a black horse.

The Prince of Milan, and many other fair and renowned
knights, fared at the hands of Zora even as the emperor's
son of Stamboul and the king's son of Caramania had fared,
and the fairy godmother's roses withered again and
again. . . .

Years and years rolled on, and not a single suitor presented
himself. The slighting reception accorded to the first became
known, and no one dared to come. In the meantime Zora
did not grow younger. She had counted on the sovereign

charms of her wealth and her beauty, but now she began to reflect, and to fear that she would die an old maid.

Then very suddenly the doge died, and soon thereafter his wife. Thus a great change came over Zora's position. She entered into full possession of lands, seas, cities, islands, ships, and harbors, of enormous wealth, and of the two crowns of Rhodes and Cyprus.

Now suitors began to come once more. The first was a great lord of Hungary. He wrote Zora a very courteous letter asking for her hand.

Zora went to consult her birds. One of them sang its habitual refrain, that Zora was more beautiful than sun or moon or stars. Zora, charmed with his singing, doubled its ration of seeds. The other bird, which had grown old, merely chirped a few incoherent words, in reward for which the Queen of Cyprus gave it a rap across the beak with her fan.

The next day Zora rose early and called her maid.

"Comb my hair," she said, "and arrange my tresses as elegantly as possible. I expect a suitor to-day. It seems that I please him, and that he is coming to try his fortune. Do your very best, and I will reward you richly. It is not, as you know, because I am a coquette, but because propriety demands that— What is the matter?" cried Zora, noticing that the maid stopped suddenly.

"Nothing, madam, nothing!"

"Nothing? One is not astonished at nothing. I wish to know what is the matter!"

"Oh, nothing, madam, nothing! Only a gray hair."

At these words Zora jumped up like one possessed.

"You lie!" she said. "Because you are red-haired, and envy my beautiful black locks, you wish to ruin my reputation. But you shall not succeed."

237

She seized the servant by her red hair and threw her out of the window.

"So much for my gray hair!" she cried, with a diabolical laugh.

The maid fell into a deep pit at the foot of the castle.

Zora hastily covered the spot where the gray hair grew with heavy jewels. Then she put on the crown of Cyprus, and went to receive the great Hungarian lord.

He was a perfect colossus in size, and well advanced in years. He limped with one foot, and squinted with both eyes; his nose was as curved as a half-moon, and his beard pointed like a crowbar; his teeth were like those of a wild boar.

"Beautiful queen," he said, "or dogeress, or princess, if you prefer it, you see that I am not quite perfection, but I hope you will excuse that. No one in this world is perfect, neither you nor I. So I don't hesitate to confess that I have a weakness for Tokay, and that——"

"Insolent wretch!" cried Zora, "how dare you present yourself before me, who am a doge's daughter, Queen of Cyprus, the honor and glory of my sex? Have you ever seen the eagle mate with the owl? Get you gone, or I will set my dogs upon you!"

The Hungarian was by no means disconcerted. He twirled his mustache majestically, and replied:

"Forsooth, the eagle will not mate with the owl, neither will the owl mate with the turkey. However, as I approached the castle I saw something fly out of the window and fall into the moat. My manners are a little brutal, but at heart I am not so bad. I sent my servants to see what it was. They found a red-haired girl, who, however, was young and pretty. She was still alive. Now that I have come in search of a wife, I dare say the red-haired girl will not set the dogs upon me."

He made a lame bow to the Queen of Cyprus, and retired.

The servant-maid, full of gratitude to her deliverer, said:

"Better to have a lame and squinting husband than none at all. If he likes Tokay, I'll try to acquire a taste for it."

So she accepted him, and they went happily off to Hungary. . . .

At last, a long, long time thereafter, a letter was received at the castle. It announced the coming of a new suitor, the Knight of Sixboards.

"What do you think of it?" Zora asked her two chaffinches.

The birds sang a flattering refrain. So their mistress was pleased, and gave them double rations. Then she called a maid, desiring to be combed and dressed against the coming of her noble guest. The maid began to comb her hair, but did so slowly and painfully.

"What is the matter?" asked Zora. "Your hands scarcely move. You know that I am in a hurry."

"Madam," replied the maid, "one cannot gather leaves on the trees in winter."

"What do you mean?"

"That it is difficult to arrange black tresses when the hair is white."

"Heaven curse you!" cried Zora. "You, too, are against me, and so envious that you will not allow my hair to be black!" And the queen strangled her maid servant with a girdle of silk, and cast her into the deepest cellar of the castle. Then, to hide the damage that the years had wrought, she placed upon her head both crowns, draped herself in a black veil, and sat upon a throne in the darkest corner of the great hall.

The suitor entered with his train. His was a fearful face. His head was bare, he had neither nose nor eyes, neither lips nor teeth. One could not say that he was only skin and bones, for he was naught but bones. Instead of arms, he bore a huge scythe. It was Death.

"Fair princess," said the sinister guest, "I have, as you perceive, none of the defects for which you drove former suitors away. My face knows not the disfigurement of a curved nose, nor of a pointed beard, nor of boar's teeth. I am neither warrior nor pedant; I neither write verses nor drink wine. So high is my rank, that counts and princes, kings and emperors, bow before me; so rich and powerful am I that all the treasures and honors of the whole world are as nothing in my sight. I have but one failing: I am a terrible vagabond. Through all the year, night and day, without rest, without ceasing, I wander through the world. I am seen north and south, on sea and land, in cities and deserts. I am received sometimes in the palaces of kings, and sometimes in the hovels of the poor. I mow down the old and the young, the beautiful and the ugly. To-day your turn has come. I am the bridegroom for whom you have waited so long, and I come to take you to my castle of Sixboards."

The daughter of the doge trembled in every limb.

"Back!" she cried, "back! I have accepted no suitor, neither will I accept you. Rather live a century without a husband than yield to you!"

"No doubt," said the inexorable suitor, "but, unhappily, it's impossible. There is no alternative for those whom I elect."

Traditional Legend

The visitor seized Zora in his arms. The chaffinches protested her fairness in song; but Death broke a window with his scythe, and carried off the royal lady.

—*Kapper's " Tales of the Dalmatian Coast."*

Bohemian Wit and Humor

Unknown Author

Beggars' Song

Up, beggars! Be joyful, for joy is our own;
Our garments are tattered, and bald is our crown.
Beloved, want presses us; what shall we do?
Why, want is one wo, discontent would make two!

Let's enter the inn, though we stay but a minute,
For the bottle looks mournful when nothing is in it;
Legs weary, bags empty, and what shall we do?
Why, bearing one burden, we need not make two!

On Friday we dine, from a halfpenny pot;
Sour broth, ragged bones, bread and water we've got.
And fish? To be sure—in the Danube, the sea,
Which are fresher and sweeter than caught fish can be.

Then Saturday comes—that's perplexing and rude—
And Sunday, with hunger; but where is the food?
We sit at the table—poor devils!—to eat;
Were the table but covered our task would be sweet!

Our cooks are sad pygmies; they cannot be less:
They needs must look small when they've nothing to dress.
Can they carve from a fog, make of darkness a stew,
Or turn a stag's ghost to a venison *ragoût?*

242

Jan Neruda

A Fiendish Plot

On August 20, 1849, at half past twelve o'clock in the afternoon, Austria was to be destroyed. This had been determined at a meeting of the Pistol Club. I cannot now recall the exact offense Austria had been committing, but I do know that we reached our decision after mature deliberation. There was no hope. The die was cast. The carrying out of the edict was left to Ziska, Prokop the Bald, Prokop the Small, and Hus. These personages were, as a matter of fact, myself, Joseph Rumpel, son of a butcher, Franz Dick, son of a cobbler, and Anton Hochmann, who was attending school in Prague at the expense of his peasant brother. The historical names here cited were not chosen by chance, but were assigned according to merit. I was Ziska, for I was the blackest man of them all, spoke most energetically, and appeared at the very first meeting of the club (held in a garret at Rumpel's) with a black bandage over one eye, which caused a general sensation. Now, this black bandage I had to wear at all our meetings. It was not very pleasant to have to do it, but then, the others had to live up to their names too.

The plan had been laid with diabolical foresight. For a whole year we put every Kreutzer we could spare into the treasury of the club, so that at last it contained eleven Gulden. For five Gulden we bought a pistol, which, the salesman assured us, was "the genuine article." We passed the pistol from hand to hand at our meetings (which, since the begin-

243

ning of the holidays, were held daily), and assured each other that it was "the genuine article." Altogether we were very careful. We admitted no new members into our club for fear of treason. We four were enough. With the other six Gulden we might have purchased another pistol and thus doubled our armament, but we had set the money aside for gunpowder, of the cost of which we had no glimmering. For our plan one pistol sufficed. Another possession of the club was a porcelain pipe, which, at the meetings, little Prokop smoked in the name of us all. It was an excellent pipe; a goblet and a spear were depicted on it; but we could assign it no part for the great day.

I publish our plan here, in order that it may win due admiration.

Our grand purpose was the destruction of Austria; the first necessity, the possession of Prague. The taking of the Belvedere was to be the means by which we were to become masters of Prague, for in that position we thought that we could not be bombarded; and we were going to storm the fortress at noon. If you consider that from time immemorial sudden surprises in war have been carried out at midnight, and that therefore all sentinels are most vigilant then, you will appreciate the devilish cunning of our innovation. Now, at that time—namely, noon—the citadel was guarded by only six or eight soldiers. Very stealthily we were to approach, we four, throw ourselves upon the sentinel, overpower him, take his gun, and then break into the guard-house, dispose of the other guards, and take their weapons. Only the second detachment of guards would then remain; they would probably yield, and then we could bind them. Should they not yield, it was their own affair if they had to be killed. Then we were to take a cannon to the gate, and cry from the battle-

Jan Neruda

ments that the revolution had begun. Of course, a lot of soldiers would come from outside the citadel; but they would not be able to scale the walls, and once a minute we would open the gate, fire off a cannon, and slam the gate to again. The soldiers who came first would thus be annihilated; the others would probably surrender, for the revolution would receive encouragement at all hands. Then we would sally forth, unite with the citizens of Prague, and liberate all political prisoners.

The rest was as simple and natural as the growing of grass. In the first battle we would defeat the army, wiping it out completely in the second. Then we would conquer Vienna, and destroy Austria. The Hungarians would help us. Then we would destroy the Hungarians.

Splendid!—"*How Austria was Saved.*"

Traditional Legend

The Fortunate Shepherd

ONE day, when the Lord was walking upon earth with
Saint Peter, they met a shepherd tending his sheep. They
were both hungry, and so they asked the shepherd to give
them some food, adding that God would reward him. The
shepherd did not know to whom he was speaking, but he had
a good heart. He drew from his wallet a large piece of
bread, which he had kept for his own evening meal, and
gave it to them.

"Eat," said he, "and may God bless you, for hunger is
a bitter thing."

The Lord and Saint Peter ate heartily. When their hunger was appeased, the Lord said to the shepherd:

"I thank you. You are a good man. You gave us your
last morsel of bread, at the risk of going hungry yourself.
Such a good act deserves to be rewarded. We will do all
we can to leave you a token of it. Make three wishes, and
all three shall be granted. But reflect carefully, lest some day
you regret your choice."

The shepherd was a great smoker; his first wish was for
a fine pipe, always lit, and never having to be refilled.
Scarcely had he uttered this wish, than he held in his hand
a superb pipe, over which floated a bluish haze of smoke.

"And your second wish?" asked the Lord.

The shepherd reflected. Saint Peter approached him and
silently pointed toward heaven. The shepherd paid no
attention. Either he did not understand, or he preferred to

246

stay here below. He remembered that he was fond of playing at dice, and that he had had but little luck at the game.

"I wish," said he, after a moment, "always to be a winner
at dice."

"It shall be according to your wish," said the Lord.
"And now the third?"

Saint Peter made signs to the shepherd, and pointed to
heaven, as before; but it was in vain.

"I wish," said the shepherd, "to have a bag into which
I can force any one to go, and keep him there till I allow
him to come out."

The Lord consented. Saint Peter was angry. "Some
day," he thought, "you will ask for salvation, and then it
will be too late."

Suddenly the Lord and Saint Peter disappeared. At first
the shepherd believed that he had been fooled by a dream;
but he saw the fine pipe, and at his side the bag made of
beautiful new leather. That put him into a good humor.
He left his sheep, and went out into the world. He went
to the right, he went to the left. Everywhere he played dice,
and since he was always winner his pockets were always
full of money. One day he came to a castle of which strange
things were related. Strange, fearful noises arose in it at
night, so that the whole house shook. The master of the
castle was a rich knight. He had it announced everywhere
that he would give a great sum to any one who would restore
peace to his castle. Many came and tried, but no one succeeded. The shepherd conceived the idea of trying. The
knight received him well, and had him led to the chamber
where most of the horrors took place. Food and drink were
given him, and he waited quite happily.

At the stroke of midnight a loud noise arose. Something

fell from the ceiling: it was a human foot! It walked toward
the shepherd.

"Ah, ah," sneered the shepherd, "why do you come alone?
Where have you left your companion?"

Another noise arose. Crack! a second foot tumbled
down.

"Where there are feet there must be hands, and where
there are hands, the rest of the body cannot be far behind."

He had hardly uttered these words when a hand fell down,
then another, then two sides of a trunk, and then a head.
All the bones joined themselves together, and a complete
skeleton stood before the shepherd.

"If that's the whole business," said the latter, "and nothing worse comes, I need not be afraid."

He had not finished these words when the skeleton began
to move. The shepherd had not time to bethink himself—a
devil stood before him. The first instant he was afraid;
but he soon came to himself again, and began observing what
the devil was going to do.

First of all the latter made a commotion that shook the
whole house.

"We will play at dice," said the skeleton; "look out that
you win. If you lose, you are a dead man, like all the others
who have ventured here before you."

"Very well, very well," said the shepherd.

And so they started to play, the shepherd always winning.
The devil became furious. Hoping to retrieve himself, he
threw a heap of ducats on the table. He lost all. Enraged,
he sprang upon the shepherd, intending to strangle him.
The latter remained unmoved, and merely cried, "Into the
bag with you!" And there was the devil in the bag. He
cried, groaned, threatened—all in vain. He had to remain

in the bag. The shepherd lay down quietly, and slept till morning.

On the following night he was at his post. This time two devils fell from the ceiling, invited the shepherd to play, lost their money to him, tried to strangle him, and were promptly clapped into the bag. The following night three devils came, one of whom was Satan in person. They fared no better, and also ended in the bag. On the fourth night nobody came.

The shepherd went to the master of the castle, who was deeply astonished. At first the shepherd's story was not believed, but he showed the horns and splay hoofs of the devils sticking out of the bag, and that was irrefutable proof. The devils were carried to the nearest smithy, and were there beaten and hammered by ten strong fellows. The devils begged and prayed for their liberty. At last the men got so tired beating them that the devils were released after they had sworn all manner of infernal oaths never to return. From that time on they were seen no more.

Nothing was now lacking to our shepherd. He had received magnificent presents, and had won an immense fortune from the devils. He lived very happily. But one fine morning Death, who forgets no one, paid him a visit. The shepherd was not thinking of death; for those who are happy do not want to die.

He received Death rudely. The latter became insistent, and was clapped into the bag.

"Let me go," said Death; "I promise to spare you."

But the shepherd was not to be moved.

Then strange things came to pass. No one died. Men and beasts accumulated like moss in the woods. Everybody asked what had become of Death. Then came a great famine,

249

and men perished without dying. The shepherd pitied their misery. He let Death go, after exacting an oath never to seek him out again.

He lived long thereafter, without any care. But at last he grew weary of life, and resolved to start for heaven. He traveled for a long time, and at last arrived at the gate of paradise. He knocked. Saint Peter appeared.

"Who are you, traveler?" he asked through the wicket of the gate.

"A good man. Let me in."

But Saint Peter recognized the shepherd.

"Impossible. You have no business here. You forgot heaven, and preferred temporal goods. I cannot give you what you have despised. Seek those with whom you have played at dice."

And Saint Peter closed the wicket.

The poor shepherd started out on the road to hell.

When he came to the door he met one of the devils whom he had beaten. This fellow raised such an alarm that the whole of hell broke loose. The guards at the gates were doubled, in order that the enemy might not enter. What was to be done now? You may well believe that our shepherd was embarrassed.

He thought it best to return to heaven and try to soften Saint Peter's heart. He shed tears, said prayers, omitted nothing to get salvation. The gatekeeper was finally moved, let the shepherd enter, and assigned him a place near himself. And since then, whenever Saint Peter sleeps, it is the shepherd who performs his duties.—*Hrase's Collection.*

Polish Wit and Humor

Kajetan Wengierski

The Dream-Wife

STRANGELY 'wildered must I seem;
I was married—in a dream.
Oh, the ecstasy of bliss!
Brother, what a joy is this!
Think about it, and confess
'Tis a storm of happiness,
And the memory is to me
Sunbeams. But fifteen was she:
Cheeks of roses red and white;
Mouth like Davia's; eyes of light,
Fiery, round, of raven hue,
Swimming, but coquettish too;
Ivory teeth; lips fresh as dew;
Bosom beauteous; hand of down;
Fairy foot. She stood alone
In her graces. She was mine,
And I drank her charms divine.

. . . .

Yet, in early years our schemes
Are, alas! but shadowy dreams.
For a season they deceive,
Then our souls in darkness leave.
Oft the bowl the water bears,
But 'tis useless soon with years;
First it cracks, and then it leaks,
And at last—at last it breaks.

Polish Wit and Humor

All things with beginning tend
To their melancholy end:
So her beauty fled.

. . . . . .

Then did anger, care, and malice
Mingle up their bitter chalice.
Riches like the whirlwind flew,
Honors, gifts, and friendships too;
And my lovely wife, so mild,
Fortune's frail and flattered child,
Spent our wealth, as if the day
Ne'er would dim or pass away;
And—oh, monstrous thought!—the fair
Scratched my eyes and tore my hair.
Naught but misery was our guest.
Then I sought the parish priest:
"Father, grant me a divorce.
Nay, you'll grant it me, of course;
Reasons many can be given—
Reasons both of earth and heaven."
"I know all you wish to say.
Have you wherewithal to pay?
Money is a thing, of course—
Money may obtain divorce."
"Reverend father, hear me, please ye—
'Tis not an affair so easy."
"Silence, child! Where money's needed,
Eloquence is superseded."
Then I talked of morals, but
The good father's ears were shut.
With a fierce and frowning look
Off he drove me— And I woke.

Henryk Sienkiewicz

On the Edge of the Abyss

THE rent of the studio which Swiatecki and I occupied in common had not been paid; first, because our resources did not amount to five rubles, and, secondly, because we had a sincere aversion to the paying of rent. We painters are often called spendthrifts, and yet I would rather spend the money for wine than squander it on a landlord. Our landlord, by the way, was by no means a bad-natured fellow, and, what is more, we had our own methods of dealing with him. Whenever he came up to dun us, which usually happened rather early in the morning, Swiatecki would half arise from his bed—a sack of straw covered by some Turkish drapery that had seen service in the background of many a painting—and say in a sepulchral voice, " Ah, I am glad to see you, for I dreamed that you were dead." The landlord, who was superstitious, and evidently afraid of death, would become confused. Swiatecki would throw himself backward, stretch out his legs, fold his hands upon his breast, and say, " This is the way I saw you lying. You had on white gloves with very long fingers, and patent-leather boots. Your appearance had not changed much." And then he was wont to add, " Such dreams do not always come true." The " not always " drove our landlord to despair. The affair ended in his growing angry, slamming the doors behind him, and rattling down the stairs cursing. But, good fellow that he was, he could never make up his mind to send us the sheriff. To be sure, there was not much that the law could have attached, and no doubt our landlord realized that if he were to let the studio and kitchen to other artists, he would fare no better, and perhaps worse.

But our means of pacifying him lost their efficacy in the course of time. The landlord accustomed himself to the idea of death. Swiatecki was just about to paint three pictures in the manner of Wuertz—*Death, Burial, Awakening*—and of course the landlord was to figure in all three. Such ghastly subjects were Swiatecki's specialty. In his own words, he painted large, small, and medium cadavers. It was probably due to this choice of subject that no one would buy his pictures, though he had talent. He had just sent two of his large cadavers to the Paris Salon exhibition, whither I had sent my *Jews Beside the Vistula,* which the catalogue had changed to *Jews by the Waters of Babylon,* and we were both impatient for the decision of the jury. Of course, Swiatecki had made up his mind beforehand that everything would turn out as badly as it possibly could. Either, he declared, the judges would prove to be complete idiots, incapable of recognizing our merits, or we should come to see that we had been complete idiots to send pictures so badly done that to distinguish them would be idiocy still more complete.

How this fellow embittered my life in the two years during which we lived together is quite beyond description. His ambition was to appear in the guise of a moral cadaver. Thus he pretended to be a drunkard, which was by no means the actual case. He would drink off two or three brandies and look round to ascertain if we had seen him. Was he not sure if we had, he would call the attention of one of us to his feat, and ask in a sepulchral voice:

"Am I not far gone?"

Henryk Sienkiewicz

We would tell him not to be silly.

Then his wrath would break out, for nothing enraged him more than to have his moral downfall doubted.

As a matter of fact, he was a thoroughly fine fellow.

Once, by the lakes of the Austrian Alps, we lost our way. Night was approaching, and there was some danger of one breaking one's neck. So Swiatecki said:

"Listen, Wladeck: you have more talent than I. It would be a pity if you were killed; so let me go first. If I fall down, you stay quietly here until to-morrow, and then you will find some way out."

"On the contrary," I replied, "I will go first, because my eyes are better than yours."

"Even if I don't break my neck to-day," said Swiatecki, "I shall do so some other time, anyhow. I don't care a straw whether it's sooner or later."

We discussed the matter and argued at length. In the meantime it grew pitch dark. At last we determine to draw lots. Swiatecki pulls the shorter straw, and goes first. We move slowly along the narrow mountain path. The path becomes narrower and narrower. To the right and left of it yawn chasms, which in all probability are very deep. And still narrower grows the path, now a mere razor ridge, from which pieces crumble off continually.

"I'm going to creep on all fours; it's all I can do now," says Swiatecki.

We soon see that no other method of progress is possible. The ridge is now no broader than the back of a horse. Swiatecki sits down astride in front, I behind him. We support ourselves with our hands on the rock before us, and thus lift ourselves along bit by bit, to the great damage of our clothes.

In a little while I hear Swiatecki's voice:

"Wladeck, we have got to the end of the ridge!"

"And what comes next?"

"An abyss, apparently."

"Take a stone and throw it down. We may judge of the depth by its sound."

In the darkness I hear my companion hunt for a loose piece of rock.

"Now listen! I am going to throw it."

We strain our ears. Not a sound!

"Did you hear anything?"

"It must be more than a hundred fathoms deep."

"Throw another."

Swiatecki takes a larger fragment and throws it. Not a sound!

"Is the place bottomless?" cries Swiatecki.

"There's no help for it. We'll have to stay here without budging till morning."

So there we are. My friend throws a few more stones, with equally unsatisfactory result. One hour passes; another. I hear Swiatecki's voice:

"Wladeck, don't go to sleep and fall off. Haven't you a cigarette?"

I have a cigarette, it appears, but not a single match. Despair!

A drizzling rain begins to fall about an hour after midnight. All about us darkness impenetrable. I realize that we who live in the midst of men, whether in town or country, have no conception of silence. The silence which now surrounds us makes us hear distinctly the rush of our own blood and the beating of our own hearts.

At first the situation is not without interest—to sit astride of a mountain ridge at night, with abysses on every side. But presently it grows cold, and Swiatecki begins to philosophize:

"What is life? Loathsome through and through. Art, forsooth—what is art? A mere aping of nature, and, furthermore, it leads to dishonesty. I have seen the Salon twice. There hang canvases without number. And what are they there for? Mere striving to satisfy possible purchasers. Anarchy! True art does not exist at all. Nature alone exists, but it is the question whether nature is not equally worthless at bottom. The best thing one could do would be to jump down and end this misery. And I would, if I had some brandy. But as I have sworn not to die sober, and as I have no brandy, I can't jump."

As a rule, I am accustomed to Swiatecki's talk, and it has very little influence on me. But here in the darkness and silence, at the edge of an abyss, his words make me gloomier still. Fortunately, he soon ends his discourse.

And then it seems to me that dawn is slowly coming. Gradually I begin to see dimly the outlines of my hands grasping the ridge and the outlines of Swiatecki's shoulders, like a black silhouette upon a slightly lighter background. And this background grows paler. An exquisite, pale-gray hue spreads among the cliffs, as if a silver fluid had been poured over them. Black has turned to gray, and gray to pearl.

It grows lighter and lighter.

I try to catch and hold in memory the wonderful blending and changing of colors, when a loud cry from my colleague interrupts me:

"Oh, what asses we are!"

His form disappears from before my eyes.

Polish Wit and Humor

" Swiatecki, what are you doing? "

" Don't bawl; come here."

I lean forward, and what do I see? I am sitting on a narrow rock that stands about a yard above a meadow. Upon the meadow the moss is so close and deep that it had deadened the sound of the falling stones. Had we slipped down, we should have been at home long ago, and not have sat all through the cold night in the open air.

—" *The Third.*"

Julian Niemciewicz

Gwiazdalska

NEAR Lenczyca, upon a flowery mound,
A proud and noble mansion looked around.
There lived a count ambitious, who aspired
To honors. He found what he desired:
The king's cupbearer he. His
Were piles of wealth, and towns and palaces.
This matters not. His pride, his boastings, were
Of his fair daughter, who was passing fair,
For bounteous Nature o'er the maiden threw
All charms men love, and all they worship too.
She was a very queen of grace, whose skill
Played with the heart, and wielded it at will.
The story of her beauty, like a breeze
Bearing sweet perfume, spread through the provinces,
Ran o'er the land, and many a raptured youth
Laid at her feet vows of eternal truth.
They saw her, and were lost. A single glance
Of that bright, lovely, laughing countenance
Pierced every heart. No wonder: the control
Of wit and beauty captures e'er the soul.
But was Gwiazdalska faultless? No; one little sin—
For she was human—one alone crept in;
One little fault or error, which, Heaven knows,
Was a dust-atom on a scarlet rose.
What might this little, trifling error be?
Time and the maiden never could agree.

She knew not wherefore years should be divided
In months and days and hours—and years derided.
She thought that Time, to please a maiden's whim,
Might tarry. Little knew the maid of him.
She deemed her smile should stop the hastening day,
When in delights and feasts it sped away,
And the wing'd hours in their swift flight restrain,
And to a rock Time's slippery spirit chain.
E'en thus she lived, and dreams like these employed
The shifting moments which those dreams enjoyed.
Her dawn was noon, Time's dawn her middle night.
She was always late; her place, though noblest, might
Remain unfilled. To table she first came
When all was over. And 'twas just the same
If at the theater was acted a new play:
Her coming till the end she'd sure delay;
Nor, going to church, would she appear before
The stately beadle closed the hallowed door.
She was her parents' hope and chiefest bliss;
And thus they never scolded her remiss.
There is great pleasure—so some people say—
Sweet pleasure in such lingering and delay;
And none of her admirers loved her less
For all her dilly-dally tardiness.
But one she did prefer unto the rest, and he
Was young Wojewodzic of Kajavy;
He bore Guzdawa's arms. And those who bear
These old insignia, history doth suppose,
Were long distinguished for their length of nose,
Their large, bright eyes, their crisp and curly hair;
Unwearied in all enterprise; in war
Supremely valiant; rather superstitious;

Julian Niemciewicz

Amorous, as born beneath love's famous star.
Indeed, our Wojewodzic was ambitious
To be a true Guzdawa, and the youth
In size, form, virtues, was their heir in sooth.
His life was stainless, and 'twas decorated
With all the gems of talent. Happy-fated,
He won the lady's promise to be his;
And parents' blessings crowned the promised bliss.
Then swam his soul in joy, and rapture threw
Her sunshine on the moments as they flew.
A month before the chosen day began
The nuptial preparations. Wild desire
Made hours—yea, each minute—as they ran,
Linger like years, whose dragging footsteps tire.
But hopes, and meditations, and soft sighs
Relieved their slothful passage as he brought
Her beauty, wit, and gentleness to thought,
The thousand graces playing round her eyes,
And her white hands, so exquisitely fair,
No ivory with their color could compare.
A hundred and a hundred times he said:
" She is, indeed, the sweetest, loveliest maid! "
And then a sad, sad thought would oft intrude:
" She's so forgetful, though so fair and good;
Surely 'tis not her fault, but Time's,
Who may, and no doubt does, mistake the time of day.
But let us wed; this weakness shall be checked;
'Tis a slight fault, and easy to correct.
Watches and clocks shall hang on every wall,
And silver hammers will each hour recall;
Hours, minutes, seconds—monitors like these
Will chase the maid's obliviousness with ease."

So he soliloquized. His doubts were gone.
The marriage contract signed, and all was done,
And the church doors were opened for the pair;
Gorgeous and fine was the assembly there.
The bridegroom sallied forth from his abode,
And no unhappy omen stopped his road.
He came with friends and relatives, who wore
Their sable furs, adorned—as well became
Those doing honor to so proud a name—
With dazzling gold and sunny scarlet o'er.

   .   .   .   .   .   .

From distant forests wagons brought vast stores
Of their wild tenants, deer and fawns and boars—
Game without number; which six master cooks,
Who wore their Gallic caps, prepared with all
The precepts given in gastronomic books.
Mince-meats and spices—but I'll not recall
The vast details. The noblest thing they did
Was to erect a mighty pyramid
Of almonds crusted o'er with sugar. Can
Aught exceed in taste a *marcypan?*
A curiously constructed lynx portrayed
The escutcheons of the bridegroom and the maid.
The table was weighed down with luxuries rare,
And all the neighbors of high rank were there,
Prelates and senators. The cupbearer vowed
To give the act its due solemnity,
And went to Skirniewicz with a crowd
Of liegemen and of vassals, for to see
The venerable primate, and entreat
That he would honor the event, and be
The officiating minister, as meet.

Julian Niemciewicz

At last the guests came. Do you wish to know
How they were bestowed? That, I trow,
'S too much for me to answer. They were driven
To rather closish quarters, but 'twas soon arranged.
The choice was to the worthy primate given;
The others, where they could, reposed their head,
And all slept soundly—some without a bed.
Then dawned the happy day. At noon,
Accompanied by pealing organ's tune,
The rings were to be changed. The friends
Were seated in the church; the clergy led
The primate, with his miter on his head,
His pastoral staff in hand, who now ascends
His throne. The tapers are enkindled. Where
Is the bride? On waiting a whole hour, they sent
To ask what cause, what luckless accident
Delayed her. Lo, here comes the messenger:
Gwiazdalska begs delay; one stocking she
Had actually got on, and speedily
Would finish with the other. Well, they wait.
Time lingers—lingers more. The clock strikes three.
They send again. 'Twas strange she should forget
The hour, she said; but she must braid her hair,
And in an eyelid's twinkle would be there.
One hour, and yet another—five o'clock,
When other heralds at her chamber knock.
She was just fixing on her robe a wreath,
And would come instantly. The well-bred sun
Tarried a little longer; then, his patience done,
He sank the occidental hills beneath.
But love had made the bridegroom angry, while
Hunger attacked the guests; their empty skin

Began to be rebellious. 'Tis a vile
Peace-breaker, that said hunger. They had thought
Of the rich feast! some little, and some naught
Had taken, and they suffered for that sin.
Oh, had they but some bread and sausage brought!
At length the ladies yawned; a senator
Opened his gasping mouth from roof to floor;
The primate was observed to whiten; then
The bridegroom rose, and to the castle fled,
Entreating on his knees the loitering maid
To hasten with her toilet. " Wait—when
I have tied this bow," the lady said, " I'll come—
I'll come indeed." He hurried back, and heard
A blending of strange sounds which struck him dumb.
He entered. First the primate's form appeared,
Sunk in the canon's arms. He looked around:
Knights and their squires were stretched upon the
  ground;
Two palatines, three barons—vanquished all
By mortal hunger. Tears of anguish fall
Down the parental cheeks. The youth's love turned cold.
" Ere thou art dressed," he said, " I shall grow old;
And if to-day thou triflest thus, to-morrow——"
He said no more, but sprung with silent sorrow
Upon his horse, and fled. Such haste was wrong;
But young men's passions are perverse and strong.
His hurry did no good; and those who marry
Should ne'er fall out with things that make them tarry.
Yet a few hours, e'en though impatient, he
Had been rewarded. 'Twas exactly three—
Three the next morning—when the lovely lady
Appeared in public, all adorned and ready.

Lettish Wit and Humor

Popular Tales

The Dogheads

In a certain forest region dogheads and men lived side by side. The former were hunters, the latter tillers of the soil. Once the dogheads caught a young girl who had come from a far country, and had lost her way in the wood. They took her to their home, and for a long time fed her with the kernels of nuts and with sweet milk. Now and then they stuck needles into the girl's arm to see if she was fat enough. The blood which flowed from her arm they licked up as greedily as a bear licks honey. At last they thought the girl was in proper condition to be eaten, so they told their mother to kill and cook her, and they themselves went out hunting. In the oven a great fire had been blazing for three days. But since there was no shovel with which the old creature could put the young girl into the oven, she sent her to the nearest human dwelling to borrow one. The girl, who had no suspicion of her fate, did as she was told, but the woman who lent her the shovel saw through the whole plan, and gave her some good advice.

When the mother of the dogheads told the girl to lie down on the shovel, the latter behaved as awkwardly as possible. She tried again and again, but could not get into the oven. Then the old creature waxed wroth and began to curse. But the girl said, "Why are you angry? Show me how it is to be done, and I will follow your example."

The advice appealed to the old monster. She lay down

flat on the shovel and cried, "Now you see!" But in the twinkling of an eye the girl shoved her into the red-hot stove, and slammed the door. Then she turned her sandals round so that toe came under heel, and fled.

When the dogheads came home they went at once for their roast and began to devour it. But somehow they did not relish it as much as they had anticipated, so that they began to look closely at the remnants, and found among them a jewel which their mother had been wont to wear. Now they realized something of what had happened, and, cursing, they set out to search for the girl. She had reached a broad river, which she found it impossible to cross. When she heard the barking and howling of the approaching dogheads, she climbed a tree, and hid herself in the foliage. The dogheads stood by the river bank, undetermined what to do. Suddenly they saw the reflection of her whom they sought in the water. A breeze had blown the leaves apart, so that the girl's face looked out, and was mirrored in the river. In their blind rage her pursuers now began to lick up the water. They licked and licked until they burst. And so the girl was safe from them forever.

—*Retold by Andrejanoff*.

Stupid Liz

THERE was once a peasant who had a beautiful but stupid wife called Liz. One day, when he was away from home, a stranger came by and asked for something to eat. The woman gave him some cabbage soup, and complained that the cabbage was not very good. She meant the cabbage-plants, and the stranger thought she meant the soup. So he said, "You must put plenty of bacon in it." When he was gone, the woman ran to the storeroom, got a great side of bacon, cut it into little pieces, and placed these on the cabbages in her vegetable garden. The neighbor's watch-dog smelling the bacon, he jumped over the fence, and began to devour the savory morsels. Then the woman grew angry, tied the dog to the plug of a beer-barrel, and beat him. Of course, the dog tugged and tugged, till the plug came out, and then he ran away with rope and plug.

What was to be done? The foolish woman ran after the dog, and at last wrested the plug from him. When she returned the beer had all run out of the barrel, and the floor was drenched. Then she remembered that there was a bushel of fine wheat flour in her cupboard. She took this out and strewed the ground with it in order to dry it. And so, when her husband came home, bacon and beer and flour were all gone.

But once his wife's stupidity helped the peasant out of a tight place. It happened that he found a treasure on a field belonging to the lord of the land. Although he commanded his wife to be discreet, she talked about it, and it came to the ears of the lord of the land, who summoned the peasant before him, and required the treasure to be given up. The peasant said that he knew nothing of any treasure, but the lord of the land cried, "Do not lie, for your wife spread the news! Come to-morrow, and bring her with you."

Sadly the peasant went home, trying to think how he could best get out of the situation. At home he said to his wife, "A great war is coming over the land. To-day the enemy will be upon us, and so we had better hide. I'll conceal myself in the woods, but do you creep into the big hole in the earth behind our house. As soon as the enemy is gone I'll come for you."

The woman climbed down; the peasant covered the opening with a cowhide, on which he strewed plentiful oats, so that ducks and geese and chickens flocked thither from all sides. They scraped and ran on the cowhide, and screamed "Ga! Ga!"

"Oh, what a frightful war they are having up there!" thought the woman. "How good that I am hidden!"

Late in the evening the peasant came, and poured warm water on the cowhide, which sickered through some holes in it. When the woman felt this she said, "Thank Heaven that it rains; the drought has lasted long."

Next morning the peasant got his wife out of the hole. "The war is over," he said. "Let us go to the manorhouse; I have some business there."

They had not gone far, when they heard the pitiful bleating of a sheep from a barn.

"Dear husband," said the woman, "what is it that groans so pitifully?"

"Let us pass quickly," said the peasant; "the devils are beating the lord of the land."

At last they came to the manor-house, and were taken before the lord of the land. He asked the woman, "Did your husband find a treasure?"

"To be sure."

"When?"

"Before the great Ga-Ga war broke out."

The lord of the land laughed. "When did that war happen?"

"At the time of the warm rain," answered the woman.

"But it has not rained for six weeks."

"Perhaps your lordship did not hear the rain, because the devils were beating you just then."

Then the lord of the land grew angry, drove man and wife forth, and so the peasant kept his treasure.

—Retold by Andrejanoff.

Servian Wit and Humor

Popular Poems

Pledges

THE wind was with the roses playing;
  To Ranko's tent it blew their leaves.
Militza, Ranko, there were staying,
  And Ranko writes, Militza weaves.
His letter done, he drops his pen;
  Her finished web she throws aside.
All anxiously doth Ranko then
  Interrogate his promised bride:
"Militza, tell me truly, now,
  Say, dost thou love me—love me best?
Or heavy is thy nuptial vow?"
  The maiden thus the youth addressed:
"Believe me, thou my heart, my soul,
  That thou art dearer far to me,
Far dearer, Ranko, than the whole
  Of brothers, many though they be,
And that the vows we pledged together
Are lighter than the lightest feather."
                    —*Vuk's Collection.*

The Ring

THE streamlet rippled through the mead, beneath the maple-
    tree;
There came a maid down to that stream—a lovely maid was
    she;

Popular Poems

From the white walls of old Belgrade the maid came
    smilingly.
Young Mirko saw, and offered her a golden fruit, and said:
"Oh, take this apple, damsel fair, and be mine own sweet
    maid!"
She took the apple, flung it back, and said, in angry tone:
"Neither thine apple, sir, nor thee! Presumptuous youth,
    begone!"

The streamlet rippled through the mead, beneath the maple-
    tree;
There came a maid down to that stream—a lovely maid was
    she;
From the white walls of old Belgrade the maid came
    smilingly.
Young Mirko saw, and offered her a golden brooch, and
    said:
"Oh, take this brooch, thou damsel fair, and be mine own
    sweet maid!"
She took the brooch, and flung it back, and said, in peevish
    tone:
"I'll neither have thee nor thy brooch! Presumptuous
    youth, begone!"

The streamlet rippled through the mead, beneath the maple-
    tree;
There came a maid down to that stream—a lovely maid was
    she;
From the white walls of old Belgrade the maid came
    smilingly.

Young Mirko saw, and offered her a golden ring, and said:
" Oh, take this ring, thou damsel fair, and be mine own
   sweet maid!"
She took the ring, and slipped it on, and said, in sprightliest
   tone:
" I'll have thee, and thy golden ring, and be thy faithful
   one!"

—Vuk's Collection.

Man, Maid, and Widow

THE king from the queen an answer craves:
" How shall we now employ our slaves?"
" The maidens shall work embroidery,
The widows shall spin flax-yarn for me,
And the men shall dig in the fields for thee."

The king from the queen an answer craves:
" How shall we, lady, feed our slaves?"
" The maidens shall have the honeycomb sweet,
The widows shall feed on the finest wheat,
And the men of maize-meal bread shall eat."

The king from the queen an answer craves:
" Where for the night shall rest our slaves?"
" The maidens shall have rooms airy and high,
The widows on mattressed beds shall lie,
And the men on nettles under the sky."

—Vuk's Collection.

Mine Everywhere

"COME with me, thou charming maiden;
Be my love, and come with me."
"Wherefore play with words so foolish?
That can never, never be.
I had rather in the tavern
Bear the brimming cup, than ever,
Ever promise to be thine."
"I am the young tavern-keeper,
So thou wilt indeed be mine."
"Wherefore play with words so foolish?
No such fate will e'er befall.
In the coffee-house I'd rather
Serve, enveloped in my shawl,
Rather than be thine at all."
"But I am the coffee-boiler,
Thee, my maiden, will I call."
"Wherefore play with words so foolish?
That can never, never be.
Rather o'er the field I'll wander,
Changed into a quail, than ever,
Ever give myself to thee."
"But I am a cunning sportsman,
And thou shalt belong to me."
"Wherefore play with words so foolish?
That can never, never be.
Rather to a fish I'd change me,
Diving deep beneath the sea,
Rather than belong to thee."

" But I am the finest network,
Which into the sea I'll cast.
Mine thou art, and mine thou shalt be—
Yes, thou must be mine at last!
Be it here, or be it there,
Mine thou must be everywhere!"

—Vuk's Collection.

Rumanian Wit and Humor

Queen Elizabeth of Rumania— "Carmen Sylva"

The Caraiman

Long, long ago, when the sky was nearer to the earth than now, and there was more water than land, there dwelt a mighty sorcerer in the Carpathians. He was as tall as the tallest pine-tree, and he carried upon his head a whole tree with green twigs and budding branches. His beard, that was many yards long, was of moss, and so were his eyebrows. His clothing was of bark, his voice was like rolling thunder, and beneath his arm he carried a set of bagpipes as big as a house. He could do anything he liked with his bagpipes. When he played softly, young green sprang up all round about him, as far as his eye could reach; if he blew harder, he could create living things; but when he blew fearfully loud, then such a storm arose that the mountains shook and the sea shrank back from the rocks, so that more land was left uncovered.

Once he was attacked by some powerful enemies, but instead of having to defend himself, he merely put the bagpipes to his lips, and changed his foes into pines and beech-trees. He was never tired of playing, for it delighted his ear when the echo sent back the sound of his music to him, but still more was his eye delighted to see all grow into life around him. Then would thousands of sheep appear on every height and from every valley, and upon the forehead of each grew a little tree, whereby the Caraiman might know which were his; and from the stones around, too, dogs

275

sprang forth, and every one of them knew his voice. Since he had not noticed much that was good in the inhabitants of other countries, he hesitated a long while before making any human beings. Yet he came to the conclusion that children were good and loving, and he decided to people his land with children only. So he began to play the sweetest tune he had ever yet composed—and behold! children sprang up on every side, and yet more children, in endless crowds. Now you can fancy how wonderful the Caraiman's kingdom looked. Nothing but play was ever carried on there; and the little creatures toddled and rolled around in that beautiful world and were very happy. They crept under the ewes and sucked the milk from their udders; they plucked herbs and fruit and ate them; they slept on beds of moss and under overhanging rocks, and were as happy as the day was long. Their happiness crept even into their sleep, for then the Caraiman played them the loveliest airs, so that they had always beautiful dreams.

There was never any angry word spoken in the kingdom of the Caraiman, for these children were all so sweet and joyful that they never quarreled with one another. There was no occasion for envy or jealousy, either, since each one's lot was as happy as his neighbor's. And the Caraiman took care that there should be plenty of sheep to feed the children; and with his music he always provided enough of grass and herbs, that the sheep, too, might be well nourished.

No child ever hurt itself, either; the dogs took care of that, for they carried them about and sought out the softest, mossiest spots for their playgrounds. If a child fell into the water, the dogs fetched it out; and if one were tired, a dog would take it upon his back and carry it into the cool shade to rest. In short, the children were as happy as though they had been in Paradise. They never wished for anything more, since they had never seen anything outside their little world.

There were not yet any " smart " or "ugly" clothes then; nor any fine palaces with miserable huts beside them, so that no one could look enviously at his neighbor's belongings. Sickness and death were unknown, too, in the Caraiman's country; for the creatures he made came into the world as perfect as a chick from its shell, and there was no need for any to die, since there was so much room for all. All the land which he had redeemed from the sea had to be populated, and for nothing but sheep and children there was room on it, and to spare, for many a long day.

The children knew nothing of reading or writing; it was not necessary they should, since everything came to them of itself, and they had to take no trouble about anything. Neither did they need any further knowledge, since they were exposed to no dangers.

Yet, as they grew older, they learned to dig out little dwellings for themselves in the ground and to carpet them with moss, and then of a sudden they began to say, " This is mine."

But when once a child had begun to say " This is mine," all the others wanted to say it too. Some built themselves huts like the first; but others found it much easier to nestle into those that were already made, and then, when the owners cried and complained, the unkind little conquerors laughed. Thereupon those who had been cheated of their belongings struck out with their fists, and so the first battle arose. Some ran and brought complaints to the Caraiman, who in consequence blew a mighty thunder upon his bagpipes, which frightened all the children terribly.

So they learned for the first time to know fear; and afterward they showed anger against the talebearers. In this way even strife and division entered into the Caraiman's beautiful, peaceful kingdom.

He was deeply grieved when he saw how the tiny folk in his kingdom behaved in just the same way as the grown people in other lands, and he debated how he might cure the evil. Should he blow them all away into the sea, and make a new family? But the new ones would soon be as bad as these—and then, he was really too fond of his little people. Next he thought of taking away everything over which they might quarrel; but then all would become dry and barren, for it was but over a handful of earth and moss that the strife had arisen, and, in truth, only because some of the children had been industrious, and others lazy. Then he bethought himself of making them presents, and gave to each sheep and dogs and a garden for his particular use. But this only made things far worse. Some planted their gardens, but others let them run wild, and then perceived that the cultivated gardens were the fairest, and that the sheep that had good pasture gave the most milk. Then the trouble became great indeed. The lazy children made a league against the others, attacked them, and took away many of their gardens. Then the industrious ones moved to a fresh spot, which soon grew fair also under their hands; or else they refused to be driven out, and long conflicts arose, in the course of which some of the children were slain. When they saw death for the first time, they were greatly frightened and grieved, and swore to keep peace with one another. But all in vain; they could not stay quiet for long; so, as they were now loath to kill one another, they began to take away each other's property by stealth and with cunning. And this was far sadder to see. The Caraiman, indeed, grew so heavy of heart over it that he wept rivers of tears. They flowed down through the valley and into the sea; yet the wicked children never considered that these were the tears their kind father was weeping over them, and went on bickering and quarreling.

Thereupon the Caraiman wept ever more and more, and his tears turned to torrents and cataracts that devastated the land, and ended by changing it into one large lake, wherein countless living creatures came to their death. Then he ceased weeping, and blew a mighty wind, which left the land dry again. But now all the green growth had vanished; houses and gardens lay buried under heaps of stones; and the sheep, for lack of pasture, no longer gave any milk; then the children cut the sheeps' throats open with sharp stones, to see if the milk would not flow out in a fresh place; but instead of milk, blood gushed out, and when they had drunk that they became fierce, and were always craving for more of it. So they slew many other sheep, stealing those of their brethren, and drank blood and ate meat. Then the Caraiman said, " There must be larger animals made, or there will soon be none left," and blew again upon his bagpipes. And behold! wild bulls came into the world, and winged horses with long, scaly tails, and elephants, and serpents. The children now began to fight with all these creatures, and thereby grew very tall and strong themselves. Many of the animals allowed themselves to be tamed and made useful, but others pursued the children and killed them; and as they no longer dwelt in such peace and safety, many grievous and dangerous sicknesses appeared among them. Soon they became in all respects like the men of other lands, and the Caraiman grew more and more soured

and gloomy, since all that which he had intended to use
for good had but turned to evil. His creatures, too, neither
loved nor trusted him, and, instead of perceiving that they
themselves had wrought the harm, thought that the Caraiman had sent sorrow upon them out of wanton cruelty and
sport. They would no longer listen to the bagpipes, whose
sweet strains had of old been wont to delight their ears.
The old giant, indeed, did not often care to play on his pipes
now. He had grown weary for very sorrow, and would
sleep for hours together under the shade of his eyebrows,
which had grown down into his beard. But sometimes he
would start up out of sleep, put the pipes to his mouth, and
blow a very trumpet-blast out into the wicked world. Hence
there at last arose such a raging storm that the trees ground,
creaking and groaning, against one another, and caused a
fire to burst out, so that soon the whole forest was in flames.
Then he reached up with the tree that grew upon his head,
till he touched the clouds, and shook down rain to quench
the fire.

But all this while the human beings below had only
one thought; how to put the bagpipes to silence forever and
ever. So they set out with lances and spears, and slings and
stones, to give battle to the giant; but at the sight of them he
burst into such laughter that an earthquake took place, which
swallowed them all up, with their dwellings and their cattle.
Then another host set out against him with pine-torches,
wherewith to set his beard on fire; he did but sneeze, however, and all the torches were extinguished, and their bearers
fell backward to the earth. A third host would have bound
him while he slept; but he stretched his limbs, and the bonds
burst, and all the men about him were crushed to atoms.
Then they would have set upon him all the mighty wild beasts

he had created; but he swept the air together and made thereof an endless fall of snow, that covered them over and over, and buried them deep, and turned to ice above them; so that, after thousands of years, when their like was no more to be seen on earth, those beasts still lay, with fur and flesh unchanged, embedded in the ice.

Then they bethought themselves of getting hold of the bagpipes by stealth and carrying them off while the giant was asleep. But he laid his head upon them, and it was so heavy that men and beasts together could not drag the pipes from under it. So at last they crept up quite softly and bored a tiny hole in the bagpipes—and lo! there arose such a storm that one could not tell earth or sea or sky apart, and scarcely anything survived of all that the Caraiman had created. But the giant awoke no more; he is still slumbering, and under his arm are the bagpipes, which sometimes begin to sound, when the storm-wind catches in them as it hurries down the Prahova valley. If only some one could but mend the bagpipes, then the world would belong to the children once more.—*"Fairy Tales." Transmitted from the Rumanian in German.*

Haytian Wit and Humor

Popular Sayings

ONLY the shoe knows if the stocking has a hole.

The rat eats the cane, and the innocent lizard dies for it.

To-day it's my turn, to-morrow it's yours.

When you dine with the devil, use a long spoon.

You can't catch a flea with one finger.

The snake that wants to live does not keep to the high-road.

You should never blame the owner of a goat for claiming it.

The ears do not weigh more than the head.

Wait till you are across the river before you call the alligator names.

If the tortoise that comes up from the bottom of the water tells you an alligator is blind, you may believe him.

A frog in want of a shirt will ask for a pair of drawers.

The ox never says " Thank you " to the pasture.

Joke with a monkey as much as you please, but don't play with its tail.

What business have eggs dancing with stones?

If you insist on punishing an enemy, do not make him fetch water in a basket.

The wild hog knows what tree he is rubbing against.

Hang your knapsack where you can reach it.

The pumpkin vine does not yield calabashes.

Every jack-knife found on the highway will be lost on the highway.

All wood is wood, but deal is not cedar.

It is the frog's own tongue that betrays him.

Popular Sayings

The same stick which beats a black dog may beat a white one.

Hunger will make a monkey eat pepper.

Accidents do not give warning, like rain.

You pretend to die, and I'll pretend to bury you.

Making a fuss is not making haste.

He who tells you to buy a horse with a big belly will not help you feed him.

A dog will never bite its pups to the bone.

If adders were not so dangerous, women would use them for petticoat strings.

If you quarrel with the highroad, which way will you go?

The spoon goes to the tray's house, but the tray never goes to the spoon's house.

If you want your eggs hatched, sit on them yourself.

Ananzi (Spider) Stories

Ananzi and the Baboon

ANANZI and Baboon were disputing one day which was fatter. Ananzi said he was sure he was fat, but Baboon declared he was fatter. Then Ananzi proposed that they should prove it. So they made a fire, and agreed that they should hang up before it, and see which would drop most fat.

Then Baboon hung up Ananzi first, but no fat dropped.

Then Ananzi hung up Baboon, and very soon the fat began to drop, which smelled so good that Ananzi cut a slice out of Baboon, and said:

" Oh! Brother Baboon, you're fat for certain! "

But Baboon didn't speak.

So Ananzi said:

" Well, speak or not speak, I'll eat you every bit to-day " —which he really did.

But when he had eaten up all of Baboon, the bits joined themselves together in his stomach, and began to pull him about so much that he had no rest, and was obliged to go to a doctor.

The doctor told him not to eat anything for some days; then he was to get a ripe banana and hold it to his mouth; when the Baboon, who would be hungry, smelled the banana, he would be sure to run up to eat it, and so he would run out of his mouth.

So Ananzi starved himself, and got the banana, and did as the doctor told him; but when he put the banana to his mouth, he was so hungry he couldn't help eating it. So he didn't get rid of the Baboon, which went on pulling him about till he was obliged to go back to the doctor, who told him he would soon cure him. He took a banana and held it to Ananzi's mouth; and very soon the Baboon jumped up to catch it, and ran out of his mouth; and Ananzi was very glad to get rid of him. And Baboons to this very day like bananas.—*Recorded by Sir George Dasent.*

Ananzi and the Lion

Once upon a time Ananzi planned a scheme. He went to town and bought ever so many firkins of fat, and ever so many sacks, and ever so many balls of string, and a very big frying-pan; then he went to the bay and blew a shell, and called the Head-fish in the sea, Green Eel, to him. Then he said to the fish, " The king sends me to tell you that you must bring all the fish on shore, for he wants to give them new life."

So Green Eel said he would, and went to call them. Meanwhile Ananzi lighted a fire, and took out some of the fat, and got his frying-pan ready, and as fast as the fish came out of the water he caught them and put them into the frying-pan; and so he did with all of them until he got to the Head-fish, who was so slippery that he couldn't hold him, and he got back again into the water.

When Ananzi had fried all the fish, he put them into the sacks, and took the sacks on his back and set off to the mountains. He had not gone very far when he met Lion, and Lion said to him:

West Indian Negro Wit and Humor

"Well, Brother Ananzi, where have you been? I have not seen you in a long time."

Ananzi said, "I have been traveling about."

"But what have you got there?" said the Lion.

"Oh, I have got my mother's bones. She has been dead these forty-eleven years, and they say I must not keep her here, so I am taking her up into the middle of the mountains, to bury her." Then they parted.

After he had gone a little way, the Lion said: "I know that Ananzi is a great rogue. I dare say he has got something there that he doesn't want me to see, and I will just follow him." But he took care not to let Ananzi see him.

Now, when Ananzi got into the wood, he set his sacks down, and took one fish out and began to eat. Then a fly came, and Ananzi said, "I cannot eat any more, for there is some one near." So he tied the sack up, and went on farther into the mountains, where he set his sacks down, and took out two fish, which he ate; and no fly came. He said, "There's no one near"; so he took out more fish. But when he had eaten about half a dozen, the Lion came up, and said:

"Well, Brother Ananzi, a pretty tale you have told me."

"Oh, Brother Lion, I am so glad you have come! Never mind what tale I have told you, but come and sit down; it was only my fun."

So Lion sat down and began to eat; but before Ananzi had eaten two fish, Lion had emptied one of the sacks. Then said Ananzi to himself:

"Greedy fellow, eating up all my fish!"

"What do you say, sir?"

"I only said you do not eat half fast enough," for he was afraid the Lion would eat him up.

Ananzi (Spider) Stories

Then they went on eating, but Ananzi wanted to revenge himself, and he said to the Lion, " Which of us do you think is the stronger? "

The Lion said, " Why, I am, of course."

Then Ananzi said, " We will tie one another to the tree, and we shall see which is the stronger."

Now they agreed that the Lion should tie Ananzi first; and he tied him with some very fine string, and did not tie him tight. Ananzi twisted himself about two or three times, and the string broke.

Then it was Ananzi's turn to tie the Lion, and he took some very strong cord. The Lion said, " You must not tie me tight, for I did not tie you tight." And Ananzi said, " Oh, no! to be sure, I will not! " But he tied him as tight as ever he could, and then told him to try and get loose.

The Lion tried, and tried in vain; he could not get loose. Then Ananzi thought, " Now is my chance." So he got a big stick, and beat him, and then went away and left him, for he was afraid to loose him, lest he should kill him.

Now there was a woman called Miss Nancy, who was going out one morning to get some spinach in the wood; and as she was going, she heard some one say, " Good morning, Miss Nancy! " She could not tell who spoke to her, but she looked where the voice came from, and saw the Lion tied to the tree.

" Good morning, Mr. Lion; what are you doing there? "

He said, " It is that fellow Ananzi who has tied me to the tree, but will you loose me? "

But she said, " No, for I am afraid, if I do, you will kill me." He gave her his word he would not; but she could not trust him. However, he begged her again and again, and said:

" Well, if I do try to eat you, I hope all the trees will cry out shame upon me."

So at last she consented. But she had no sooner loosed him than he came up to her to eat her, for he had been so many days without food that he was quite ravenous; but the trees immediately cried out, " Shame! " and so he could not eat her. Then she went away as fast as she could, and the Lion found his way home.

When Lion got home he told his wife and children all that had happened to him, and how Miss Nancy had saved his life; so they said they would have a great dinner, and ask Miss Nancy. Now when Ananzi heard of it he wanted to go to the dinner; so he went to Miss Nancy, and said she must take him with her as her child; but she said " No." Then he said, " I can turn myself into quite a little child, and then you can take me "; and at last she said " Yes." And he told her, when she was asked what pap her baby ate, she must be sure to tell them it did not eat pap, but the same food as every one else. Accordingly they went, and had a very good dinner, and set off home again. Somehow, though, one of the Lion's sons fancied that all was not right, and he told his father he was sure the baby was Ananzi; and the Lion set out after him.

Now, as they were going along, before the Lion got up to them, Ananzi begged Miss Nancy to put him down, that he might run; which he did, and he got away and ran along the wood, and the Lion ran after him. When he found the Lion was overtaking him, he turned himself into an old man with a bundle of wood on his head; and when the Lion got up to him, he said, " Good morning, Mr. Lion "; and the Lion said, " Good morning, old gentleman."

Then the old man said, " What are you after now? " And

the Lion asked if he had seen Ananzi pass that way; but the old man said, " No; that fellow Ananzi is always meddling with some one. What mischief has he been up to now?"

Then the Lion told him; but the old man said it was no use to follow him any more, for he would never catch him; and so the Lion wished him good day, and turned and went home again.—*Recorded by Sir George Dasent.*

Ananzi and Quanqua

QUANQUA was a very clever fellow, and he had a large house full of all sorts of meat. But you must know he had a way of saying *Quan? Qua?* (How? What?) when any one asked him anything, and so they called him Quanqua. One day, when he was out, he met Atoukama, Ananzi's wife, who was going along driving an ox, but the ox would not walk. So Atoukama asked Quanqua to help her, and they got on pretty well till they came to a river, when the ox would not cross through the water. Then Atoukama called to Quanqua to drive the ox across, but all she got out of him was " *Quan? Qua? Quan? Qua?* "

At last she said:

" Oh, you stupid fellow, you're no good! Stop here, and mind the ox, while I go and get help to drive him across." So off she went to fetch Ananzi.

As soon as Atoukama was gone away, Quanqua killed the ox, and hid it all away where Ananzi should not see it; but first he cut off the tail, then dug a hole near the riverside and stuck the tail partly in, leaving out the tip. When he saw Ananzi coming, he caught hold of the tail, pretending

289

to tug at it as if he were pulling the ox out of the hole. Ananzi, seeing this, ran up as fast as he could, and tugging at the tail with all his might, fell over into the river; but he still had hold of the tail, and contrived to get across the water, when he called out to Quanqua:

"You idle fellow, you couldn't take care of the ox, so you sha'n't have a bit of the tail!" and then on he went.

When he was gone quite out of sight, Quanqua took the ox home, and made a very good dinner.

Next day he went to Ananzi's house, and said Ananzi must give him some of the tail, for he had got plenty of yams, but he had no meat. Then they agreed to cook their pot together: Quanqua was to put in white yams, and Ananzi the tail and red yams. When they came to put the yams in, Quanqua put in a great many white yams, but Ananzi only put in one little red cush-cush yam. Quanqua asked him if that little yam would be enough. He said, "Oh, plenty! I don't eat much."

When the pot boiled, they uncovered it, and sat down to eat their shares, but they couldn't find any white yams at all; the little red one had turned them all red. So Ananzi claimed them all, and Quanqua was glad to take what Ananzi would give him.

Now, when they had done eating, they said they would try which could bear heat best. So they heated two irons, and Ananzi was to try first on Quanqua; but he made so many attempts, that the iron got cold before he got near him. Then it was Quanqua's turn, and he pulled the iron out of the fire and poked it right down Ananzi's throat.

—*Recorded by Sir George Dasent.*